ODYSSEUS
COMES HOME
FROM THE SEA

ODYSSEUS
COMES HOME
FROM THE SEA

Told by

ANNE TERRY WHITE

Illustrated by Arthur Shilstone

THOMAS Y. CROWELL COMPANY   New York

CROWELL HERO TALES
Lilian Moore, Editor

THE HORN OF ROLAND
told by Jay Williams
ODYSSEUS COMES HOME FROM THE SEA
told by Anne Terry White
ROBIN HOOD OF
SHERWOOD FOREST
told by Ann McGovern
THE SWORD OF KING ARTHUR
told by Jay Williams

TO CLAIRE

CONTENTS

1. On the Beach 1
2. Calypso Lets Odysseus Go 14
3. Nausicaa 19
4. In the Halls of King Alcinous 25
5. Royal Entertainment 31
6. "I Am Odysseus" 42
7. Odysseus Tells His Adventures 46
8. Homeward Bound 61
9. Under the Olive Tree 67
10. A Loyal Thrall 76
11. Father and Son 84
12. Down to the City 93
13. Stranger in His Own House 101
14. Beggar Against Beggar 109
15. Odysseus Provokes Eurymachus 116
16. Penelope and the Stranger 121
17. The Scar of the Boar 130
18. "I Myself Will Be the Prize" 136
19. Odysseus Bends the Bow 146

20.	Four Against All	153
21.	Athene Keeps Her Promise	161
22.	Husband and Wife	167
23.	Laertes	175
24.	"Let Peace and Abundance Be Their Portion"	181
Glossary		189

ODYSSEUS
COMES HOME
FROM THE SEA

Scylla

Land of the
Cyclopes

Ogygia

WHERE
ODYSSEUS
WANDERED

Land of the Cicones

Thesprotia

Mt.
Olympus

Troy

eacia

Ithaca

Same

cynthus

Pylos

Sparta

Knossos

Crete

Land of the
Lotus-Eaters

1

ON THE BEACH

Odysseus sat upon the pebbly beach, strain-ing his eyes over the empty sea. If he might so much as see the smoke curl upward from his own land! Longing for his wife and home filled his mighty heart, and he desired to die.

But rugged Ithaca was far—he did not even know in which direction his home lay—and this woodland isle was out of the way of sea traffic. Never in the seven years that the nymph Calypso had held him in her hollow caves had he glimpsed a single sail.

How he hated war! War had robbed him of everything that men held dear. What cared he that mighty Troy lay in ruin, that its defenders were dead, its women carried off? He had felt no hatred for the Trojans when he left Ithaca and had none now. In another man's quarrel his life had been wasted.

Odysseus counted up the years. Nearly twenty had gone by since the day men came to summon him to war. He was young then, rejoicing in the best the gods could grant— a kingly home, a loving wife, an infant son, parents, friends. He had no slightest wish to make war on folk who had done him no injury. A prince of Troy had stolen beautiful Helen, wife of King Menelaus of Sparta! So now all the princes of Greece and the isles must go to war to bring her back? Not he! Not for nothing did men call him wily Odysseus! He would pretend that he was mad.

That day he had done what no sane man would do. Yoking together an ass and an ox, he had gone out to plow and begun sowing salt. But one of the guests had cleverly exposed his trick. He had laid the infant Telemachus

in the path of the plow—and then there was nothing left to do but turn the plow aside to save the child. It was plain Odysseus was no madman.

After that there could be no hanging back. And was not he indeed responsible for the busy mustering to war? Had not he himself caused the chiefs to come to Menelaus' defense? All the Achaean princes had wooed Helen, and he among them. They had quarreled while waiting for her choice. "Let us not quarrel," he had said. "Instead let us swear to stand by Helen's choice and defend the rights of the successful suitor."

All the princes had made the vow, and he

with the rest. Now Helen had been stolen, and they who had sworn the vow must come to Menelaus' defense. The other chieftains were gathering their forces against Troy. He must gather his.

So he had gone, doubting that he would ever set foot in Ithaca again. Heavy forebodings troubled his spirit.

"Penelope," he had said, bidding his wife a last farewell, "I do not know if the gods will let me return. For the Trojans, too, they say, are good spearmen, and bowmen, and drivers of fleet horses. So have a care for all these things: While I am far away, be yet more mindful of my father and my mother in these halls than even now you are. But when you see your son a bearded man, then marry whom you will and leave your own house."

Nearly twenty years ago he had set sail . . .

The child Telemachus was no child now. He was a man, with the first soft beard coming on his face. And what of wise Penelope? Had she wed another? . . .

Senseless, needless, cruel war! None but the gods profited by it. The gods set men at odds for their own ends, to make amusement for themselves, to revenge themselves on one another.

"Yet once you are faced with war," Odysseus reflected, "what can you do but fight and use your wits to win?"

They had fought nearly ten years to bring down Troy, and many a brave man on either side had died in vain. But the walls of Troy still stood, and when the Trojans mounted them and looked toward the sea, they still saw the black Achaean ships beached upon the shore. Long years of war had settled nothing.

Then in a moment of inspiration he addressed the chiefs in council. "Let us win by trickery," he said, "for it is clear we cannot win by force of arms." And he proposed the building of a great, hollow wooden horse to be filled with chosen warriors, himself among them. The Achaeans would leave the wooden horse upon the beach, set fire to their huts, and pretend to sail away. The Trojans would drag the prize in triumph to their city. At night, while Troy lay sleeping, the trap door would be opened. The warriors would creep forth and

raise the war cry. Meanwhile the Achaean ships would have returned—and Troy, attacked within and without, would fall.

So the wooden horse was built and filled with fifty chosen men. The trap door was shut tight—none outside could see there was a door. Then came the night. The Achaeans drew their black ships down to the sea, the rowers sat in order on the benches, and the sails bellied in the breeze.

After the long night, morning. And with the morning came the Trojans, pouring out of their gates with shouts of joy. From the walls

they had seen the empty beach, the black ships gone. Before them now was the broad stretch of plain where the enemy camp had stood. Gone were the huts, the horses, chariots, all. Ashes, rags, bones, the litter of an army camp, lay strewn about. And on the shore stood a huge horse of wood.

Warily the Trojans approached, then examined it with mounting curiosity. On one of its sides they saw words cut in large letters: IN THANKFUL ANTICIPATION OF A SAFE RETURN TO THEIR HOMES THE ACHAEANS DEDICATE THIS OFFERING TO THE GODDESS ATHENE.

While the warriors inside the hollow horse held their breath, the priest Laocoon read the words aloud. Then clamor broke out. Some cried, "Let us cleave it with our spears!" Others said, "Drag it to the brow of the hill and hurl it from the rocks!" But the greater number shouted, "Take it into the city!"

"What madness is this!" the priest chided. "Do you think the Achaeans are to be trusted? Have you not had enough experience of them to fear even their gifts?" And grasping the nearest warrior's spear, he thrust it angrily into the belly of the horse. The men inside quaked at the hollow sound that came from the wood, but the Trojans were too excited to notice it.

Just then an Achaean, trembling and wailing, was haled before King Priam. "Ah me!" the captive sobbed. "Where shall I go? For the Achaeans have abandoned me and the Trojans will slay me!"

Odysseus recognized the voice of his cousin Sinon, who had volunteered to stay behind to signal the ships, now hidden behind a nearby island. Odysseus himself had carefully taught

Sinon what to say and now waited to hear more.

"Who are you?" Priam asked.

"Sinon am I, an unfortunate man whom the Achaeans intended to sacrifice to get a fair wind home. The princes were all tired of the war. They would have departed long ago if the winds had not been contrary. The soothsayer chose me for the sacrifice, and all the rest said yea, for each man was glad he had not been chosen. They were just going to take my life when the wind changed of itself. And in the confusion of the launching I was forgotten and escaped and hid myself."

"And what is the meaning of this wooden horse?" the king demanded.

"It is an offering to Athene," replied Sinon. "Ever since Odysseus stole the statue of the goddess from your temple, Athene has withheld her favor from us. Three times the stolen statue was enveloped in flames. Also we saw sweat pouring from its limbs. So when the princes decided to leave, they built this horse, to be a peace offering to the daughter of almighty Zeus. Thereby they thought to get a safe journey home."

"But why," Priam asked, "did you make the horse so big?"

"That you Trojans might not be able to take it through the gates of your city," Sinon replied. "For if you did, Athene would give her protection to you, not us. Then *you* might even invade *our* shores and take *our* cities."

The Trojans were completely deceived by the story. So wheels were quickly brought, and with great effort the huge horse was dragged up. As Sinon had said, it was too big to get through the gates. The wall had to be breached. But what did that matter now, when the enemy had departed?

The Trojans were wild with joy. The war was over, the victory theirs! Till late in the night Odysseus and his companions heard the people celebrating. But when at last all slept, Sinon softly rose, slipped out of the city, and lit a beacon high up on a mound. Afterward he cautiously made his way to the wooden horse and knocked on the belly as Odysseus had instructed him. . . .

Sitting on the pebbly beach and looking out over the blue water, Odysseus relived the ex-

citing moments following that knock. The
bolts slid back. Warily he put out his head,
looked about, and dropped the ladder. One by
one the warriors climbed down. The loud war
cry rang out—and the sleeping city awoke to
slaughter, fire, and pillage. There was no beat-

ing back the Achaeans now, for the returning host poured through the breach in the wall so lately made. In fire and smoke, amid the groans of the dying and the lament of the living, great Troy fell.

And then? Then Menelaus had taken his Helen home upon his beaked ship. And Odysseus himself had sailed away with many ships and many men. Now all were gone, some had been slain upon the land, some were lying on the deep sea bottom. He alone of all his men remained, prisoner of the nymph Calypso.

"It is as the gods will," Odysseus sighed, wiping away a tear. "All my guile has not served me."

He had been too clever, he told himself. Unwittingly on his homeward way he had offended Poseidon, god of the sea, by blinding his one-eyed son. Now a terrible curse lay upon him. The dread words rang in his ears: "Grant that Odysseus, son of Laertes, may never come to his home in Ithaca! Yet if he is ordained to see his own friends and country, let him come late, with the loss of all his company, in the ship of strangers, and find sorrows in his house!"

He had got used to sorrows. Oh, that he might but see the smoke curl upward from his own land!

2

CALYPSO LETS ODYSSEUS GO

"Odysseus!" called a voice behind him, and turning, he saw Calypso picking her way over the shining pebbles. He did not rise.

"Unfortunate man," she said tenderly when she saw his gloomy face, "sorrow no more. For now I will send you off with all my heart. Arise and cut long beams and make a wide raft that it may bear you over the misty deep. I will give you bread, and red wine, and water to keep hunger far away. And I will send a fair wind that you may come all unharmed to your own country."

He stared at her, bewildered. He could not believe that she, who had so long tempted him to be her husband, had suddenly decided to let him go. "There must be some trick here," he thought, and rising, scanned her face. He did not guess that gray-eyed Athene had at long last pleaded for him before the gods. How could he know that on high Olympus it had been decided to bid Calypso let him go?

"It is plain, goddess," he said warily, "that you have some other thought in this. Why do you bid me cross in a raft the dread and difficult sea which even the swift, gallant ships do not pass over rejoicing? Nay, I will not go aboard a raft to please you. Not unless," he added, "you swear a great oath not to plan anything secret to do me harm."

Smiling, she said: "Let the earth and the wide heaven above and the falling water of the Styx be witness that I will not plan any secret thing to do you hurt."

It was the mightiest of oaths!

Half-doubting still, in the early dawn Odysseus took from Calypso's hand a great double-edged ax of bronze and a polished adze and followed her to the border of the isle where tall trees grew. His mighty muscles bent to the task as he swung the ax. Twenty trees he felled and trimmed and smoothed. He bored each piece, and jointed them together. And he set up a mast and a rudder and fenced his craft against the waves. Meanwhile the nymph brought him cloth to make sails, and these too he fashioned very skillfully. And at last he pushed the raft with levers down to the sea.

Four days this took Odysseus. And lo, on the fifth, the nymph placed on board two skins of wine and one of water, bread in a bag, and dainties of all sorts. She sent a warm and gentle wind to blow. And he rejoiced as he set his sails to the breeze.

For seventeen days Odysseus sailed on the wine-dark sea, cunningly guiding his craft with the helm. And on the eighteenth day there rose before him the shadowy hills of the land of the Phaeacians.

But now the god Poseidon spied the raft

and helmsman from afar. The king of the sea was mightily angered in spirit, for he had not been present at the council of the gods when Athene had pleaded for Odysseus. He gathered the clouds, shrouding land and sea, and stirred up the water. The great waves smote the raft till it reeled. This way and that it was swept on the deep as the north wind sweeps thistledown along the plain. Then with a groan the timbers broke apart, leaving Odysseus astride a single beam. Stripped of all his garments, for two days and nights he clung to the wood. At last a great wave bore him to the shore, and there by a river's mouth he lay, without breath or speech, swooning with weariness.

But presently his strength returned. He staggered up into a wood near the shore, crept under the bushes, and covering himself with fallen leaves, fell asleep.

3

NAUSICAA

Now as Odysseus lay there, a band of maidens came down to the river with lovely Nausicaa, daughter of King Alcinous. The princess had risen early to go a-washing. She had asked her father for a wagon, and piling her soiled garments and those of her father and brothers upon it, had driven the mules to the river while her attendants followed on foot.

Briskly the maidens trod the clothes in the water to cleanse them. Afterward they spread them out on the clean pebbles to dry. And when they had bathed and taken their midday meal, they fell to playing at ball. Now it chanced that Nausicaa threw the ball to one of her company and missed, so that the ball fell into the deep, eddying current. At this all raised a piercing cry. Then Odysseus awoke and sat up.

"Woe is me! To what men's land have I come now?" he moaned. "By that shrill cry of maidens, I think I am near men of human speech."

He crept out and, breaking a leafy bough, held it across his body to hide his nakedness. Thus he advanced. But when the maidens saw him, they fled, so terrible did he seem in their eyes, all marred with the salt sea foam. Only the daughter of Alcinous stood firm.

Then Odysseus spoke words, sweet and cunning, as he so well knew how: "O queen, great awe comes upon me as I look on you, for never have my eyes beheld such a one among mortals. If indeed you are not a goddess but are of the

daughters of men who dwell on earth, thrice
blessed are your father and your lady mother,
and thrice blessed your brothers. Surely their
souls glow with gladness each time they see
so fair a flower of maidens in the dance. But he
is blessed beyond all others who will prevail
with gifts of wooing and lead you to his home."

Nausicaa listened, and in her heart was
strange commotion, for never yet had she
heard a man speak so.

"Yesterday, on the twentieth day," Odysseus
said, "I escaped from the wine-dark deep. And
now some god has cast me on this shore that
here too some evil may befall me. But, queen,
have pity on me, for after many sore trials I
have come to you first. Show me the way to the
town, and give me an old garment to cast
about me. And may the gods grant you all
your heart's desire: a home and a husband,
and a mind at one with his—a good gift, of
all things the best."

"Stranger," Nausicaa answered him straightway, "you shall not lack garments, nor anything else that is the due of an unfortunate
suppliant. I will show you the way to the town
and name the name of the people. The
Phaeacians hold this city and land, and I am
the daughter of King Alcinous." Then she
called to her maidens: "Halt! Why do you flee
at sight of a man? This is some helpless one
come here in his wanderings. Give the stranger
food and drink and bathe him in the river in
some place with shelter from the wind."

At that the maidens returned. They took
Odysseus to a sheltered place and made him

sit down, and laid a mantle and a tunic beside him, and gave him soft olive oil in a jar.

Then Odysseus said: "I pray you, stand apart while I myself wash the brine from my shoulders and anoint myself with olive oil. For I am ashamed to make myself naked in the company of maidens."

So they went apart and told all to their lady. And when Odysseus had washed his whole body and anointed himself and dressed, he went to the shore of the sea. There he sat down, glowing with beauty and grace so that the princess marveled at him.

"He is like the gods that keep the wide heaven," Nausicaa said to her maidens. "Would that such a one might be called my husband and that it might please him to remain here!"

Then she bade them set meat and drink beside Odysseus, and he ate and drank eagerly. Afterward she said: "Up now, stranger, and let me bring you to the house of my wise father. But do just as I tell you. So long as we are passing along fields and farms, walk quickly with the maidens behind the wagon, and I will lead the way. But when we approach the city, sit down in the poplar grove near the road. Wait there. And when you think we have reached the palace, go into the city and ask for the house of my father.

"For there are many insolent folk among the people, and some might meet me and say: 'Who is this that goes with Nausicaa, this tall and goodly stranger? He will be her husband. Truly she does not care for the Phaeacians, the many noble men who are her suitors.' Thus they will speak.

"But, stranger, mind well what I say that you may get an escort at my father's hands and a safe return. When you have come to the palace of Alcinous, pass quickly through the great chamber. Go to Arete my mother, who sits in the light of the fire, weaving. Pass by my father's throne and cast your hands about my mother's knees. If she be kindly disposed toward you, then there is hope that you will see your friends and come to your own country."

She spoke and struck the mules with the whip.

4

IN THE HALLS
OF KING ALCINOUS

Odysseus did as Nausicaa bade him. He
found the house of her father and passed
quickly over the threshold into the palace.
Certain captains and counselors of the Phaeacians were in the great hall. But the goddess
Athene shed a thick mist around him, so that
he passed unnoticed through the throng till
he came to Arete and the king. Then Odysseus
cast his hands about the knees of the queen,

and the wondrous mist melted from him, and a silence fell on all at sight of him.

"Arete, queen," he began his prayer, "after many trials I have come to your husband and to your knees and these your guests. May the gods give them a happy life and may each one leave to his children the wealth in his halls. But I pray you, speed my parting, that I may come the more quickly to my own country. For already too long do I suffer distress far from my friends."

With that he sat down in the ashes at the fire. But King Alcinous took Odysseus by the hand and sat him on a shining chair. A handmaid brought water in a golden ewer and poured it over his hands into a silver basin. Presently a grave housedame brought wheaten bread and set it on a table by him. Upon the board, too, she laid many dainties, giving freely of such things as she had by her. So Odysseus ate and drank.

Then Alcinous said to his henchman: "Mix the bowl and serve the wine." And when he had served it out to all and they had drunk to their hearts' content, the king addressed the company:

"Hear me, you captains and counselors of the Phaeacians. In the morning let us call more elders together and entertain the stranger. After that we will get a convoy ready, that this stranger may speedily reach his own country." He paused and looking hard at Odysseus, added, "But if he is some deathless god come down from heaven, then the gods are planning some new evil against us."

"Alcinous, let that thought be far from you!" Odysseus quickly cried. "I am but a man. Whomsoever you know that is heaviest laden with sorrow, to him I might compare myself. I pray you, bestir yourselves early in the morning that you may set me upon my country's soil. Ah, and may life leave me when I have had sight of my possessions, my thralls, and my dwelling that is great and high!"

So he spoke, and they all agreed to set him on his way. After that they poured out wine to the gods and went each one to his house. But Odysseus was left behind in the hall, and Queen Arete and King Alcinous sat beside him.

Now Arete spoke first, for she recognized the mantle and tunic Odysseus wore, having herself made them with her women. "Sir," she said, "I am bold to ask you first of this. Who are you of the sons of men and where do you come from? Who gave you these garments? Did you not say that you came here wandering over the sea?"

Then Odysseus answered her and said: "It is hard, O queen, to tell my griefs from end to end, for the gods of heaven have given me griefs in plenty. But this I will tell you: Zeus with his white bolt crushed my swift ship and cleft it in the midst of the wine-dark deep.

There all the rest of my good company was lost, but I clung about the keel of the ship, and so was borne for nine whole days. And on the tenth dark night the gods brought me to the isle of Ogygia. There dwells the nymph Calypso, a crafty goddess.''

Odysseus then went on to tell how the nymph had held him captive seven years on her seagirt isle but never won his heart; how she had sent him away at last; how Poseidon had shattered his raft; and how when he wakened on the shore he had seen Nausicaa with her company of maidens and begged her grace.

"She gave me bread and red wine and let me wash myself in the river," Odysseus ended, "and she gave me these garments. This is all the truth."

"Sir," Alcinous answered him, "surely this was not right of my daughter. She should have brought you to our house with her handmaids since you came to her first."

And Odysseus said: "My lord, do not blame the maiden. For indeed she told me to follow with her company. But I dared not, fearing you might be angry at the sight."

"Sir, my heart is not of such temper as to have been angry without a cause," Alcinous said. "Would that so goodly a man as you would wed my daughter and be called my son and remain here. I would give you a house and wealth if you would stay. But against your will none of the Phaeacians shall keep you. You shall have an escort tomorrow. My young men will row till you come to your country, though it be farther than the farthest land men know. You shall see for yourself how sturdy are my ships and how my young men excel at tossing the salt water with the oar-blade."

So they spoke. And Arete bade her hand-maids set out a bedstead for the stranger under the gallery. There he slept. And it seemed to him that rest was wondrous good.

5

ROYAL
ENTERTAINMENT

When it was early dawn, King Alcinous rose
from his bed and led his guest to the assembly
place of the Phaeacians, close by the ships.
And when all the captains and counselors were
gathered, Alcinous said to them:

"Hear me, you captains and counselors of
the Phaeacians. This stranger—I know not
who he is—has come here in his wandering
and asks for a convoy. So let us speed it on.

31

For never does any man stay here long in sorrow for want of help upon his way. Come, let us draw a black ship down to the sea, and let there be chosen fifty and two noble youths who have proved the best. When they have made the oars fast upon the benches, let them all step ashore and come to my house and quickly fall to feasting.

"This is the command I give to the noble youths. But you others, sceptered kings, come now with me that we may entertain the stranger in my halls. And let no man make excuse. Moreover, bid the blind minstrel Demodocus come, for the god has given him minstrelsy as to no other."

He spoke and led the way, and the sceptered kings went with him while the henchman went to get the minstrel. And when the fifty and two chosen youths had drawn the ship down, and set up the mast, and fixed the oars in the leather loops, and spread the sails, they moored her in the shore water. After that they went to the great palace of Alcinous.

The galleries and the courts and the rooms were thronged with men who came to the gathering. Alcinous sacrificed twelve sheep, and eight boars, and two oxen. They skinned these and prepared a goodly feast.

Then the henchman led in the beloved minstrel and set a high chair for Demodocus in the midst of the guests, placing it against a tall pillar. He hung the lyre on a pin close above the blind man's head and showed him how to lay his hands on it. And close by him the henchman placed a basket, and a table, and a goblet of wine to drink when his spirit bade him.

So they reached for the good food spread before them. But after they were satisfied, the minstrel was moved to sing a famous lay. The song was about Odysseus, about the bitter quarrel he had once had with the hero Achilles. And Odysseus, listening, caught his great purple cloak with his hands and drew it down over his head. For he was ashamed to shed tears in front of the Phaeacians. And none of all the company saw him weeping— only Alcinous noted it.

Presently the king said: "Hear me, you captains and counselors of the Phaeacians! Now that our souls have been satisfied with the good feast and with the lyre, let us go out and show the stranger how greatly we excel all men in boxing, and wrestling, and leaping, and running."

He spoke and led the way to the place of the assembly. A great company of people went with them, and there many noble youths stood up to play.

First they held a foot race. And Clytoneus, son of Alcinous, was far the swiftest of them all in running. Then they made trial of wrestling and leaping and weight throwing and boxing.

Now when they had all taken their pleasure in the games, Laodamus, the eldest son of Alcinous, said to his companions: "Let us ask the stranger whether he is skilled in any sport." And going up to Odysseus, he himself addressed him, saying: "Father and stranger, come and try your skill in the sports, too, if you are practiced in any. Come, try! Cast away care! Your journey will not be long delayed —see, your ship is even now drawn down to the sea, and the men of your company are ready."

But Odysseus answered him: "Laodamus, why do you mock me, requiring this thing of me? Sorrow is far nearer my heart than sports. For I have endured much, and now I sit in your gathering longing for my return."

Then Euryalus, who had excelled at the wrestling, rebuked Odysseus to his face, saying: "Nay, truly, stranger, I do not think you are one who is skilled in games. Rather are you such a one as comes and goes in a trading ship, a master of sailors that are merchantmen, one with concern for his cargo and greedily gotten gains. You do not seem to be a man of sports."

Then Odysseus looked fiercely on him and said: "Stranger, you are presumptuous. You have stirred my spirit by speaking thus amiss. I am not unskilled in sports, but I have endured much in passing through wars and the grievous waves of the sea. Yet even so, I will try the games, for your word has bitten me to the quick."

So saying, he leaped to his feet and caught up a huge weight, heavier far than those the Phaeacians had been casting. With one whirl he sent it from his stout hand, and the stone

flew hurtling. The Phaeacians crouched to the earth under the rushing of the stone. Beyond all the marks it flew, so lightly did it speed from his hand.

"Now reach this throw, young men, if you can," Odysseus said. "And I will cast another after it, as far or yet farther. And whosoever will, let him come and contend with me in boxing, or in wrestling, or even in the foot race. I care not which, for you have greatly angered me. I am no weakling in the feats of men. In archery I declare myself far more excellent than any mortal now on earth. And with the spear I can throw farther than any other man can shoot an arrow. Only in the foot race some of the Phaeacians may outstrip me. For I have been shamefully broken in many waters."

So he spoke, and all kept silence. Alcinous alone answered him: "Stranger, your words are not ill taken in our gathering, you being angry that this man taunted you. We are not perfect boxers, nor wrestlers, but speedy runners and the best of seamen. Lo, arise now, you dancers of the Phaeacians, the best in the land

and make sport, so that the stranger may tell his friends when he returns home how far we surpass all men in seamanship and speed of foot and in dance and song."

So they leveled the place for the dance. And the henchman led Demodocus with his lyre into the midst of the ring, and round him stood young boys skilled in the dance. They smote the level ground with their feet. And Odysseus gazed at the twinkling of the feet and marveled.

Then Alcinous bade his sons Halius and Laodamus dance alone, for none could match them. They took a ball of purple hue, and one would bend backward and throw it toward the shadowy clouds, and the other would leap upward and catch it lightly in his turn before his feet touched the ground. Afterward they set to dance, tossing the ball from hand to hand, and the other youths stood by and beat time, and a great din arose.

"My lord Alcinous," Odysseus said then, "you boasted that your dancers are the best in the world, and your words are fulfilled. I wonder as I look at them."

Alcinous was pleased by his words and said: "Hear me, you captains and counselors of the Phaeacians! This stranger seems to me a wise man. Come, then, let us give him a stranger's gift. There are twelve glorious princes who rule among this people, and I myself am the thirteenth. Now each man among you bring a fresh robe and a tunic, and a talent of gold. Let us speedily carry all these gifts together, that the stranger may take them in his hands and go to supper with a glad heart. As for Euryalus, let him make amends to the man himself with soft speech and with a gift, for his was no gentle saying."

All agreed, and each one sent his henchman to fetch his gift. And Euryalus answered the king and said: "My lord Alcinous, I will make amends to your guest. I will give him a sword all of bronze with a silver hilt and a sheath of ivory."

With that he put the rich gift in Odysseus' hands, saying: "Hail, stranger and father! If anything offensive has been spoken, may the storm winds soon snatch and bear it away. But may the gods grant that you see your wife and come to your own country and your friends."

Then Odysseus answered him: "You, too, my friend, all hail! May the gods give you happiness, and may you never miss this sword which you have given me, you who with soft speech have made me amends."

He spoke and hung the silver-studded sword about his shoulders. And the sun sank, and the noble gifts were brought him. The henchmen bore them to the palace. There Alcinous told Arete to bring a fine chest for the gifts and to add to them yet another fresh robe and tunic.

"And I," he said, "will give our guest a beautiful golden cup of mine, that he may remember me all the days of his life when he pours the drink offering to Zeus and to the other gods."

So Arete brought a coffer from the treasure chamber and laid the gifts in it. At her bidding Odysseus closed the box and tied the hasp with a knot of rope to make all safe. Then he went to be with the chiefs at their wine.

And, behold, Nausicaa stood by the pillar of the roof.

"Farewell, stranger," she said to him, "and even in your own country think of me for to me first you owe the ransom of your life.

"Nausicaa, daughter of Alcinous," Odysseus answered her, "may Zeus the thunderer grant that I reach my home. There would I worship you as a goddess all my days, for you, lady, have given me my life."

He spoke and sat down in the high seat by King Alcinous. They were serving out the portions and mixing the wine.

6

"I AM ODYSSEUS"

Now, when all had eaten and drunk to their hearts' content, Odysseus spoke to the blind minstrel and said: "Demodocus, I praise you far above all mortal men. For you can chant all that the Achaeans did and suffered as if you had been present. Come now, sing of the making of the horse of wood, the guileful thing that goodly Odysseus filled with the men who wasted Troy."

Then the minstrel showed his minstrelsy. He took up the tale where it tells how one part of the Achaeans set fire to their huts and went aboard their ships and sailed away, while the others were hidden in the horse, in the assembly place of the Trojans. And he sang how the Achaeans poured forth from the horse and sacked the city.

Odysseus' heart swelled as he listened. Tears ran pitifully down his checks: But none of the company saw him weeping—only Alcinous noted it as he sat near and heard him groaning heavily.

Presently the host said to the company: "Hear me, you captains and counselors of the Phaeacians! Now let Demodocus hold his hand from the loud lyre. For this song of his is by no means pleasing to all. From the time that the divine minstrel was moved to sing, this stranger has never stopped lamenting. Sore grief has seized upon his heart. Now let the minstrel cease, that we may all alike be merry, hosts and guest."

Then turning to Odysseus, he said: "All things are ready for you, honorable stranger, the convoy and the gifts, which we give out of our love. Therefore do not hide anything that I would ask you. Say what is the name they call you by at home. Tell me, too, of your land, and your city, that our ships may know their course to bring you there. Tell us plainly where you were borne in your wandering. Say, too, why you weep and mourn at the tale of Troy. Had you a kinsman by marriage that fell before that famed city? Or else some loving friend, a good man and true? For a friend with an understanding heart is no whit worse than a brother.''

Then Odysseus answered him: "King Alcinous, most notable of all the people! Truly it is a good thing to listen to a minstrel such as this one, like the gods in voice. Nay, as for me, I say that there is no more gracious delight than when men sit orderly at feast in the halls and listen to a singer, and the tables by them are laden with bread and meat, and a wine bearer pours wine into the cups. This seems to me well-nigh the fairest thing in the world. But now you have asked about my grievous troubles. What, then, shall I tell of first, what last? For the gods of heaven have given me woes in plenty.

"Now first, I will tell you my name. I am ODYSSEUS, SON OF LAERTES, who am noted for all manner of wiles, and my fame reaches to heaven. I dwell in Ithaca, a rugged isle, but a good nurse of noble youths. And for myself, I think there is nothing sweeter than a man's own country, even though he live in a rich home in a strange land. But come, let me tell you of the trials of my journeying, which Zeus laid on me as I came from Troy."

7

ODYSSEUS TELLS
HIS ADVENTURES

Silence fell as Odysseus leaned forward in his high seat. Eagerly the Phaeacians looked upon his noble face and form. The minstrel held the lyre soundless on his knees, and vainly fixed his blind eyes on the far-famed man whose deeds he had so often sung.

"The wind that bore me from Troy," Odysseus began, "brought me near the Cicones. I sacked the city and slew the people, and we took their wives and much wealth and divided them among us. After that I commanded that we should quickly flee. But my men in their folly would not listen.

"Meanwhile the Cicones raised a cry to other Cicones, their neighbors who dwelt inland, and in the morning they gathered thick as leaves. They set their battle in array by the swift ships, and the hosts cast at one another with their bronze-shod spears. So long as it was day, we beat them off. But when the sun was going down, the Cicones drove us in and overcame us. And six of my company perished from every ship.

"We sailed from there sad at heart, yet glad as men saved from death, although we had lost our dear companions.

"Now Zeus, gatherer of the clouds, aroused the north wind against our ships. We lowered the sails in fear of death and rowed landward. There for two nights and two days we lay, but on the third day we set up the masts and hoisted the white sails. And now I should have come safely to my own country but the north wind swept me from my course.

"For nine whole days I was borne by fierce winds over the deep. But on the tenth day we set foot on the land of the lotus-eaters, who eat a flowery food. I chose three of my men to search out what manner of folk they were. Now, the crafty lotus-eaters, meeting them with guile, gave my men some of the lotus to taste. And when they had tasted the honey-sweet fruit, they had no more wish to come back, but chose to remain there and ever feed on the lotus. Therefore I led them back to the ships weeping and much against their will, and dragged them under the benches, and bound them in the ships. And I commanded the rest to go on board. So they smote the gray sea water with their oars and we sailed onward till we came to the land of the Cyclopes.

"There is an isle outside the harbor of that land, on which are numberless wild goats. We landed there at night and slept on the beach. All the next day we spent shooting goats and looking across at the smoke that rose on the mainland. But on the second dawn I said: 'Stay here, all the rest of you, while I go with my company to see what manner of folk they are.'

"As soon as we had landed, we saw a cave near the sea with a high stone court around it. I chose twelve good men and set out, taking with me a goatskin of dark, sweet wine that once a priest of Apollo had given me.

"Presently we came to the cave. We gazed on all that was inside—baskets full of cheeses, and folds crowded with lambs and kids, and milk pails and bowls swimming with whey.

My company begged me to take some of the cheeses, then drive off the kids and lambs to the swift ships, and sail away. But I would not listen—I wanted to see the man himself.

"After a time we kindled a fire and took some of the cheeses and ate. Then we sat waiting till the man should come back with the flocks. But when we beheld him, we fled in terror to a hidden place in the rock. For he was not like any man that lives by bread. He was a giant, marvelously made, with one eye alone set in the middle of his forehead.

"He threw a heavy load of dry wood inside the cave. Next he drove in those of his fat flocks that he milked, leaving the rams and he-goats outside in the yard. Then he lifted a huge doorstone that twenty four-wheeled wagons could not move, and set it in the mouth of the cave. That done, he milked the ewes and goats, and then under each ewe he placed her young. Afterward he curdled half the milk and stored it in wicker baskets. The other half he let stand in pails that he might have it to drink at supper time.

"Then spying us, he asked: 'Strangers, who

are you? Where do you sail over the wet waves? On some trading enterprise, or are you sea robbers?'

"So he spoke, but as for us, our hearts shrank in terror at his deep voice and his monstrous shape. Yet I answered, saying: 'Lo, we are Achaeans, driven wandering from Troy. And we come to your knees, if perchance you will give us a stranger's gift. Nay, lord, have regard to the gods, for we are your suppliants, and Zeus is the avenger of suppliants, Zeus the god of the stranger.'

"So I spoke, and at once he answered out of his pitiless heart: 'You are witless, my stranger, who bid me fear the gods. The Cyclopes pay no heed to Zeus nor to the other gods, for verily we are better men than they. But tell me, where did you leave your ship? Was it perchance at the far end of the island, or near by, that I may know?'

"So he spoke, but I answered him with words of guile: 'As for my ship, Poseidon broke it to pieces, for he cast it upon the rocks at the border of your country. But I with these my men escaped from utter doom.'

"He answered me not a word, but sprang up and laid his hands upon two of my fellows and dashed them to earth. Then he cut them up and made ready his supper, devouring entrails and flesh and bones with their marrow. Afterwards the Cyclops drank milk and stretched out among his sheep.

"My first thought was to pluck my sharp sword from my thigh and stab him in the breast. But my second thought restrained me. For I saw that we should not be able to roll from the door the heavy stone which he set there. So in sorrow we waited for the bright dawn.

"Now when dawn came, the Cyclops kindled his fire and milked his flocks, then again seized two men and made ready his midday meal to take out with him. After that he moved away the great doorstone, drove out the flocks, and set the stone back.

"When he had gone, I was left devising evil in the deep of my heart. And this was the counsel that showed best in my sight. There lay a great club of the Cyclops in the cave, like the mast of a ship of twenty oars. I cut off a fathom

of it and set my fellows to sharpening it to a point. Then I hardened the point in the bright fire and hid everything under the dung. And I bade my company cast lots which four should risk the adventure with me.

"In the evening he came, shepherding his flocks, and all was as before save that he drove all his flocks in. Then he seized two more of my men and made ready his supper.

" 'Cyclops,' I cried then, holding in my hands a bowl of the dark wine, 'take and drink wine after your feast of man's meat, so that you may know what manner of drink we had on our ship.'

"He took the cup and drank it off and said: 'Give it to me again, and tell me your name, that I may give you a stranger's gift. For this is nectar and ambrosia.'

"So I handed him the dark wine a second and yet a third time, and he drank it down. Afterward I said: 'Cyclops, you ask me my name, and I will tell it to you. Then grant me a stranger's gift as you promised. Noman is my name.'

"And straightway he answered me out of

his pitiless heart: 'Noman, I will eat you last. That shall be your gift.'

"With that he sank backward and fell asleep with face upturned. Then I thrust that stake under the deep ashes. When the point began to glow terribly, I drew the bar from the coals. And my fellows seized it and thrust the sharp point into his eye, while I from my place on a rock above twirled it around like a drill.

"There was a great hissing, as when an ax is tempered in water. The Cyclops raised a terrible cry so that the rock rang around, and we fled in fear, while he plucked out the brand bedabbled in blood. Then, maddened with pain, he threw it from him and called with a loud voice on the Cyclopes who dwelt about him in the caves along the windy heights.

"They flocked together from every side.

" 'What has distressed you,' they asked him, 'that you cry thus aloud in the night and make us sleepless? Surely no mortal is driving your flocks against your will? Surely none slays you by force or craft?'

" 'My friends,' he roared, 'Noman is slaying me by guile!'

" 'If no man is violently handling you, then you must be sick, and sickness is sent by mighty Zeus. Pray to your father, the lord Poseidon.'

"So they spoke and departed. And my heart within me laughed to see how my name and cunning counsel had beguiled him. But the Cyclops, groaning with pain, groped with his hands and lifted away the stone from the door of the cave. Then he sat down in the entry with arms outstretched to catch anyone that was going out with his sheep—so witless did he hope to find me. But I took counsel with myself, and this was what seemed best in my sight:

"Quietly I lashed together the rams of the flock three by three. Under the middle one of each three I lashed a man, and the other two rams protected him on either side. As for me, I laid hold of a young ram who was far the best of the flock, and curled under his shaggy belly. There I clung upward, grasping the wondrous fleece, with a steadfast heart. And we waited for the bright dawn.

"As soon as it was dawn, the Cyclops let the

rams out to pasture. He felt along the backs of all as they passed out and never guessed that my men were bound under his thick-fleeced flocks. Last of all the ram to which I clung went forward.

"The Cyclops laid his hands on him and spoke, saying: 'Dear ram, why are you the last of all the flock to go from the cave? You never used to lag behind, but now you are the very last. Surely you are sorrowing for the eye of your lord, which an evil man blinded, even Noman, who I say has not yet escaped destruction.'

"With that he sent the ram out. Now, when we had gone but a little way, I first loosed myself and then set my fellows free. Swiftly then we drove those sheep till we came to the ship. And a glad sight we were to our fellows. So we embarked, and the men smote the gray sea water with their oars.

"Then I shouted to the giant, taunting him: 'Cyclops, your evil deeds have found you out, you who were not ashamed to eat your guests within your gates!'

"When the Cyclops heard my words, he

broke off the peak of a great hill and threw it at us. It fell in front of the dark-prowed ship, and the wave rose so high that it drove the ship back to the shore. Then I caught up a long pole and thrust the ship from off the land, and the men bent to the oars and rowed on.

"But when we had made twice the distance we had before, I called to him again: 'Cyclops, if any mortal man shall ask you who blinded you, say it was Odysseus, the waster of cities, son of Laertes, whose dwelling is in Ithaca.'

"With a moan he answered me: 'Lo, now the ancient oracle is fulfilled. But I always looked for some tall and goodly man to come and blind me, not a dwarf! Nay, but come here, Odysseus, that I may set a stranger's cheer before you, and that the Earth-Shaker himself may speed you on your way. For the Earth-Shaker Poseidon is my father.' And stretching his hands to heaven, he prayed: 'Hear me, Poseidon! If I am indeed your son, grant that Odysseus, son of Laertes, may never come to his home in Ithaca! Yet if he is ordained to see his own friends and country, let him come late, with the loss of all his company, in the ship of strangers, and find sorrows in his house!'

"Then once again he lifted up a stone, far greater than the first, and hurled it. But it fell behind the ship, all but striking the rudder. The sea heaved under the fall of the rock, but the wave bore the ship away from the shore.

"We soon came to the island where my other ships were. And early next day we sailed on, sad at heart, yet glad as men saved from death, although we had lost our dear companions."

8

HOMEWARD BOUND

All sat spellbound throughout the shadowy hall as Odysseus paused. Then Alcinous said: "Odysseus, you have told your tale with skill, as when a minstrel sings. I could stay in the hall till the bright dawn, so long as you would keep on telling these woes of yours."

Odysseus answered him: "There is a time for words and there is a time for sleep. But if you are eager still to listen, I will not grudge to tell you of the other things that befell me."

So he took up the tale again, and ever fresh wonder came upon the hushed Phaeacians. He spoke of wind and wave and beetling rocks; of sweet-voiced Sirens whose clear song enchants the sailor; of monstrous Scylla with six yelping mouths; and of the fair witch Circe, who turned his men to swine. Lastly he told how in the blindness of their hearts his companions slew and ate the sacred oxen of the Sun and roused the wrath of heaven.

"Zeus cast his bolt upon the ship," Odysseus ended. "She reeled all over and was filled with sulfur, and my company fell out of the vessel. Like seagulls they were borne around the black ship upon the billows. And the god took from them their day of returning. But I, clinging to the mast, was borne nine days by powerful winds, and on the tenth night the gods brought me near the isle of Ogygia. There dwells the nymph Calypso, who took me in and treated me kindly. But why tell this tale again? Yesterday I told it to you, Alcinous, and to your noble wife. And I do not like to tell twice a plain-told tale."

Then Alcinous answered: "Odysseus, you

have been sore distressed. But now you shall not be driven out of your way again before reaching home. And this is my word to you who in these halls ever drink the dark wine and listen to the minstrel. The garments for the stranger and all the gifts which you brought here for him are already laid up in a chest. But come now, let each of us give him a great tripod and a caldron besides, and we in turn will gather goods among the people and get recompense."

So spoke Alcinous, and the saying pleased them well. They rose and went each to his house and lay down to rest. But at dawn they hastened to the ship with their gifts of bronze. And King Alcinous himself went about the ship and diligently stowed the gifts under the benches that they might not hinder any of the crew in their rowing.

Afterward they went to the house of Alcinous and fell to feasting. Among them the divine minstrel played his lyre. But Odysseus would ever turn his head toward the splendor of the sun, as one who would hasten its setting. For he was most eager to return. And when he

saw the sunlight fading, he said to the Phaeacians, and to Alcinous in chief: "My lord
Alcinous, most notable of all the people, pour
the drink offering and send me safe upon my
way. And as for you, fare you well. For now I
have all that my heart desired—an escort and
loving gifts. May the gods of heaven give me
good fortune with them, and may I find my
noble wife in my home with my friends unharmed. And for your part, may the gods give
you all manner of good, and may no evil come
near the people."

Then the henchman mixed the wine and
served it to all in turn, and they poured forth to
the gods. After that Odysseus rose and placed in
Arete's hand his two-handled cup and said:
"Fare you well, O queen, all the days of your
life, till old age comes and death, that visit all
mankind. I go homeward, and you—rejoice in
your children and your people and Alcinous
the king."

With that, Odysseus stepped over the threshold, and Alcinous sent a henchman to guide
him to the ship. Behind him came maidens of
the household, one bearing a fresh robe and a

tunic, another the strong chest, and yet another bread and red wine. And when they had come down to the sea, the good men of the escort took these things and laid them in the ship.

Then they spread a rug and a linen sheet for Odysseus on the decks in the hind part of the ship that he might sleep soundly. He climbed aboard and lay down in silence, while they sat on the benches. And they unbound the hawser from the pierced stone.

As soon as they leaned backward and tossed the sea water with the oar blade, a deep sleep fell on Odysseus, a sound sleep, very sweet. And like a yoke of four stallions leaping high under the lash, so leaped the stern of that ship. The dark wave rushed mightily in the wake, and she ran ever surely on her way. Nor could a circling hawk, the swiftest of winged things, keep pace with her. Lightly she sped and cut the waves of the sea.

9

UNDER THE OLIVE TREE

While Odysseus slept, the ship neared
Ithaca. The Phaeacians knew well the haven
with the long-leaved olive tree at the harbor's
head. They shipped their oars, and the vessel
ran ashore half her keel's length. The crew
alighted. Lifting Odysseus all as he was in the
sheet of linen and the rug, they laid him sleeping on the sand. Then taking out the gifts
which their countrymen had given him, they
set them in a heap by the trunk of the olive tree
and rowed away.

Presently Odysseus awoke. He looked about him and he did not know his native land. Each thing seemed strange to him: the long paths, and the sheltering haven, and the steep rocks, and the trees in their bloom. So he started up and stood moaning: "Woe is me! To what land have I come now? And where am I taking all this treasure? Ah, the false Phaeacians have carried me to a strange land, though they promised to take me to Ithaca!"

With that he began counting the tripods and the gold and the garments. All was there, but he wailed for his native land and walked lamenting by the sea.

Of a sudden he saw a young man standing by a rock. Now this was Athene, but Odysseus did not recognize the goddess. "Friend," he said, approaching, "hail to you, and may you meet with no ill will. Tell me true. What land, what people is this? What men dwell here?"

"You must be witless, stranger," Athene answered him, "if you do not know that this is Ithaca. Its fame has reached even to Troyland, which men say is far from this Achaean shore."

Then Odysseus was glad. Yet he spoke craft-ily, saying: "I have heard tell of Ithaca even in broad Crete, far over the seas." And he went on to tell a fanciful tale of murder and escape and how Phoenician sailors had left him sleep-ing on the shore.

Athene smiled, then suddenly changing in-to a woman fair and tall, she said: "Crafty must he be who would outdo you in guile, Odysseus! So, even in your own country you do not cease from knavish words, which you love from the bottom of your heart! But come, no more of this, for both of us are practiced in deceits. You did not know me, Athene, who am always near you and guard you in all ad-ventures. I have come here to contrive a plot with you and to hide away the goods the noble Phaeacians gave you. Moreover, I will ac-quaint you with all the sorrows in your house. But tell no one, neither man nor woman, that you have indeed returned from wandering."

Odysseus answered her: "It is hard, goddess, for any mortal man to recognize you, for you take every shape upon you. But this I know well: that so long as we Achaeans made war in

Troy, you were kindly toward me. But after we sacked the steep city of Priam, never have I seen you coming on board my ship to keep sorrow from me."

"I had no mind to be at strife with Poseidon," Athene answered shortly. "But now I will not leave you in your grief, Odysseus. See, there is the cavern where you offered many a sacrifice to the nymphs. Let us set your goods in that secret place that they may remain safe for you."

With that she plunged into the shadowy cave, searching out the chambers of the cavern. Meanwhile Odysseus brought up his treasure. He laid it all inside with care, and Athene set a stone against the cave's mouth. Then they sat down under the sacred olive tree.

"Know, Odysseus," the gray-eyed goddess began, "that all the noblest of Ithaca and the islands roundabout woo your fair wife. Yet constant Penelope will choose no one of them, still hoping against hope for your return. Some years ago I put a thought into her mind how to hold off her suitors. So she set up a mighty web, and at this she would weave, saying it was a shroud for old Laertes. (For alas! your lady mother is dead and your father now lives apart on his upland farm.)

" 'Wait patiently,' Penelope told the suitors, 'till I finish this robe for Laertes.'

"They all consented. So in the daytime she wove the mighty web and in the night unraveled it, and thus for three years she held them off till at last one of her women told the secret. Then she finished the shroud, but still will make no choice. Meantime the suitors eat and drink daily in your halls, continually slaying your sheep and goats, your swine and cattle, drinking your wine and reveling.

"In vain," the goddess said, "did your son Telemachus beg the proud suitors, saying, 'Busy yourselves with other feasts. Eat your own substance or go in turn from house to house.' They laughed at him, for Telemachus did not yet know how to be master in his own house." She herself had gone disguised, Athene said, and given him counsel that he might have honor in his house and in the world of men. "Call an assembly," she had told the youth. "Put your case before the Achaean lords and call the gods to witness. Then go seek news of your father. Go first to Pylos to old Nestor and then to Menelaus, for he was the last of all the Achaeans to come home from Troy."

Telemachus had acted on her words. The lords of Ithaca had done nothing to restrain the suitors. But he was gone now to seek news of his father.

"Meantime," Athene said, "the suitors—and chief among them Antinous and Eurymachus—are darkly plotting to slay your son. They have dispatched a ship which even now lies in wait behind a wooded island. They mean to fall upon him on his homeward way. And this Penelope knows, for the henchman Medon secretly brought her news of it.

"And now, son of Laertes," Athene ended, "think how you may stretch forth your hands upon the shameless suitors, who lord it through your halls and devour your livelihood while they woo your wife."

"Lo, now, in very truth," Odysseus said, "I would have perished in my halls had not you, goddess, told me everything. Come then, counsel me how I may requite the suitors. And you yourself stand by me as you did that day when we sacked Troy. I would war even with three hundred men if you, lady and goddess, helped me the while."

Then Athene said: "I will be near you. But come, I will make you such that no man shall know you. And first of all, go to the swineherd who tends your swine and who is a loyal thrall and loves your son and Penelope. You will find him sitting by the swine near the rock of Corax. Stay there by the swine and find out all while I go to Sparta to call Telemachus, who is seeking news of you at the house of Menelaus. I will send him to you."

"But why did you not tell him about me yourself?" Odysseus said. "Was it perchance that he too may wander in sorrow over the seas?"

"Let him not lie heavy on your heart," Athene answered. "Truly the young men lie in wait, eager to slay him. But this shall never be."

So saying, she touched him with her wand. And lo! His flesh withered, and his yellow hair wasted from his head, and his eyes dimmed.

Then she changed his clothing to a torn and filthy wrap, stained with foul smoke. Over all she cast a great bald hide of a stag, and gave him a staff and an old tattered scrip, and a cord to hang it by.

After this they parted. Athene went to Sparta to fetch Telemachus, and Odysseus turned his face to the upland.

10

A LOYAL THRALL

Odysseus went up from the haven by a rough track and found the loyal swineherd sitting at the door of his hut. There in a great courtyard stood the sties in which six hundred brood swine were penned at night. And by the wall lay four dogs, fierce as wild beasts, that the swineherd himself had bred.

Now he was fitting sandals to his feet from a good brown oxhide, while the rest of the swineherds, three in all, were out with the droves of swine. The fourth he had sent to the city to take a boar to the proud suitors.

Of a sudden the baying dogs saw Odysseus and ran at him, yelping. Then Odysseus warily sat down and let the staff fall from his hand. Yet there by his own homestead he would have suffered sad hurt had not the swineherd hastened after the dogs and driven them this way and that with a shower of stones.

"Old man, truly the dogs came near being the death of you," the swineherd Eumaeus said. "So should you have brought shame on me, who have other griefs enough. Here I sit, mourning and sorrowing for my godlike lord and feeding his fat swine for others to eat. And he, meantime, begs his food, perchance, wandering over some land of men of strange speech—if he is yet alive. But come into the house with me, old man. When your heart is satisfied with bread and wine, you too may tell your tale and say where you come from and how many woes you have endured."

With that he led Odysseus into the hut and sat him down, and strewed thick brushwood

under him. Over it he spread the hide of a
shaggy wild goat, which served him for a mat-
tress. And Odysseus rejoiced that he had given
him such welcome.

"May Zeus, O stranger, and all the other
deathless gods grant you your dearest wish," he
said, "since you have received me so heartily!"

"Guest of mine," the swineherd answered
him, "it would be wrong to slight a stranger.
For all strangers and beggars are from Zeus.
And even a little gift from a thrall like me is
dear. Ah, had my master grown old at home,
he would have loved me diligently and given
me something of my own—a house and a par-
cel of ground, and a comely wife. But, alas, he
went to Troy."

So saying, he quickly stepped to the sties and
brought out two sucking pigs, and sacrificed
them both, and singed them and cut them
small and spitted them. When he had roasted
all, he set it by Odysseus, and sprinkled white
barley meal upon it. Then in a bowl of ivy
wood he mixed water with the honey-sweet
wine, and himself sat down opposite and bade
him fall to.

"Eat now, stranger, such fare as thralls have at hand," he said. "But the fatted hogs the suitors devour, for they have no pity. Every day and every night they feast—and wine they draw and waste it riotously. Ah, his wealth was great past telling. No lord in the dark mainland had so much. Nor any in Ithaca itself. Nay, not twenty men together have wealth so great."

So he spoke while Odysseus ate and drank in silence. But when he had comforted himself with food, he said: "My friend, who was it that bought you with his wealth? Tell me. Perchance I may know him, a man so very rich and mighty as you say."

"Old man," Eumaeus answered, "no wanderer comes to Ithaca but that he goes to my mistress and tells her he has seen her lord. And she receives him kindly and asks about everything, and the tears fall from her eyelids. Quickly enough would you too invent a tale if anyone would but give you a mantle and a tunic. But as for Odysseus, dogs and swift birds have torn his skin from his bones already, or the fishes have eaten him in the deep."

Then Odysseus spoke again and said: "My friend, though you say that he will not come again, I will tell you, not lightly but with an oath, that this same year Odysseus will return. As the old moon wanes and the new is born, he will return to his home and take vengeance on all who here dishonor his wife and noble son."

Eumaeus only sighed. "Drink in peace, old man," he said, "and do not bring these thoughts to my remembrance. He will never come to his home. Yet oh, that Odysseus may come according to my desire and the desire of Penelope and of that old man Laertes and godlike Telemachus! But now I lament for the boy, for he is gone to Pylos to get news of his father, and the lordly suitors lie in wait for him on his way home." He sighed again, then shook the heavy thought from him and said: "Come, old man, tell me of your own troubles and tell me true: Who are you of the sons of men? Where is your city?"

"Now I will tell you all most plainly," Odysseus replied. And he spun out a long tale such as he loved to tell—of wind and wave and drifting on a mast, of rescue and royal entertainment. Of Odysseus, too, he spoke, saying that in the land of the Thesprotians he had sure news of him. Indeed, a ship was drawn down to the sea and a company ready to convey the hero home.

"Ah, wretched guest," Eumaeus said when Odysseus ended, "you have stirred my heart with the tale of all these things. Yet, as regards my lord's return, I think you do not speak aright. Never will you persuade me with the tale about Odysseus."

While they were talking thus, the swine and the swineherds drew near. They shut up the swine to sleep in their sties, and themselves entered the hut. Then Eumaeus bade his fellows bring in one of the boars to sacrifice for a guest of his from a far land. And when the flesh was roasted and all sat down to supper, the swineherd gave Odysseus the portion of honor, the long back of the white-tusked boar.

Now the night came on foul with no moon, and it rained the whole night through, and the great west wind was blowing. So Eumaeus set a bed for Odysseus near the fire and threw skins of sheep and goats upon it. Then, when his guest lay down, he cast a great thick mantle over him. There Odysseus slept, and the young men slept beside him. But Eumaeus had no mind to lie in a bed away from the boars. Slinging his sharp sword over his shoulder and catching up a thick fleece, he went out, spear in hand, ready to defend himself against dogs and men. He would lie where the white-tusked boars were sleeping under an overhanging rock.

And Odysseus was glad because Eumaeus had great care for his master's wealth while he was far away.

11

FATHER AND SON

All the next day Odysseus stayed in the swineherd's hut. On the third day at dawn Eumaeus had just sent the herdsmen off with the droves of swine and was making breakfast ready for his guest when Odysseus heard footsteps outside. Yet he noticed that the dogs did not bark.

"Eumaeus," he said, "some friend of yours will soon be here, for the dogs do not bark but fawn around, and I catch the sound of foot-steps."

While the words were yet on his lips, his own dear son stood at the gate. The swineherd sprang up in amazement, and the vessel in which he was mingling water with the wine fell out of his hands. He ran to his master. Falling on his neck, Eumaeus kissed him all over as one escaped from death. And he wept aloud, saying: "You are come, Telemachus, a sweet light in the dark. I thought I should never see you again after you had gone in your ship to Pylos. Enter, dear child, that my heart may be glad at the sight of you in my house."

"I sent my ship and my companions on to the city," Telemachus said. "But I have come here to see you and hear from your lips whether my mother is yet in the halls or already wedded."

"Truly your mother is yet in your halls and spends day and night in shedding tears," Eumaeus answered and took from the young man his spear of bronze.

Telemachus passed into the hut. As he came

near, Odysseus rose from his seat to give him place. But the youth stopped him.

"Be seated, stranger," he said, "and we will find some other seat in our house."

Tears welled up in the father's eyes, but he restrained them. He went back and sat down, while the swineherd busied himself strewing green brushwood for Telemachus and putting a fleece on top. Next Eumaeus set fragments of yesterday's roast meat before them, and wheaten bread heaped in baskets, and wine in a goblet of ivy wood. So they ate, the three of them together.

When they had done, Telemachus said to the swineherd: "Father, where did this stranger come from?"

"My son, I will tell you all the truth," Eumaeus answered. "He comes from wide Crete, and he says that he has wandered round many cities of mortals. But now that he has come to my hut, I will give him to you for your man. Do with him as you will—he is your suppliant."

"Eumaeus, this is a bitter word you speak," Telemachus said. "How shall I receive this

guest in my house? I am young and do not yet
trust to my strength to defend me against those
who do violence without cause. I will give him
a mantle and a tunic, a two-edged sword, and
shoes for his feet, and send him on his way
wherever his heart and spirit bid him go. Or,
if you like, keep him here in the hut and take
care of him, and I will send garments and food
for him here. But into the company of the
suitors I would not have him go, for they will
mock at him, and that would be a sore grief to
me. But now, Eumaeus, go quickly and tell my
mother that she has got me safe. As for me, I

will tarry here. And when you have told the news to my mother, come back. Let no one else learn that I am here, for there are many that devise mischief against me."

"I mark, I heed, all this you speak to one with understanding," Eumaeus answered. And binding his sandals under his feet, he went away.

Now Athene saw Eumaeus pass from the hut, and she drew near in the shape of a woman fair and tall. She stood opposite the doorway of the hut so that Odysseus alone saw her—and also the dogs, who did not bark but with a low whine shrank cowering to the far side of the hut. Athene made a sign to Odysseus, and he went out of the room, past the great wall of the yard, and stood before her.

"Son of Laertes," the goddess said, "now is the hour to reveal yourself to your son. Tell him all your plans."

So saying, Athene touched him with her wand. First she cast a fresh linen robe and tunic about him. Then she increased his stature. His color grew fresh again, and his cheeks filled out, and the beard spread thick around his chin. Thus he entered the hut. And Telemachus looked—and looked away for fear that he looked upon a god.

"Stranger," he exclaimed, "you are different from what you were a moment since! And you have other garments! And the color of your skin is no longer the same! Surely you are a god. Be gracious, I pray you, and spare us that we may offer you sacrifices and golden gifts."

"I am no god, Telemachus," Odysseus answered him. "I am your father, for whose coming you have sorely groaned." With that he kissed his son and let a tear fall to earth.

But Telemachus, not yet believing, said: "You are not my father—some god is deceiving me. For no mortal could contrive this by his own wit. A moment ago you were old and foully clad, but now you are like the gods who keep the wide heaven."

"Telemachus, do not marvel overmuch," Odysseus said. "Lo, I, all as I am, after sufferings and much wandering, have come in the twentieth year to my own country. It is Athene who has made me look like this."

With that he sat down again. But Telemachus, flinging himself upon his father's neck, wept aloud. And long their tears mingled.

At last Telemachus said: "And in what manner of ship, dear father, did sailors at length bring you here to Ithaca?"

"My child, the Phaeacians brought me here," Odysseus said. "They bore me sleeping over the seas and set me down in Ithaca, and gave me splendid gifts, bronze and gold and woven clothing. These treasures are lying by the gods' grace in the caves. But now I have come here prompted by Athene that we may take counsel regarding our foes. Come, tell me the number of the suitors that I may know how many they are and whether we two will be able alone to subdue them without aid, or whether we should seek the help of others."

Then Telemachus said: "Truly, father, I have heard of your great fame—a warrior mighty and wise in counsel. But how can two men do battle with so many? For the suitors are not barely ten, nor twice ten only, but many a ten more. From Dulichium there are two and fifty chosen lords, and six serving

men go with them; and out of Same four and twenty men; and from Zacynthus there are twenty lords; and from Ithaca itself full twelve men of the best, and with them Medon the henchman, and the minstrel, and two squires skilled in carving meat. How can we alone en-

counter all these? Think, if you can, of some
champions—of any that may help us with all
their hearts."

Odysseus answered him: "Yea, I will tell
you now. Consider whether Athene and Father
Zeus will be enough for us two, or whether I
should look about for some other champion."

"These two you name are valiant helpers indeed!"

"Yet these two will not be far from us,"
Odysseus said, "when the trial of might is held.
Now go you home and stay with the proud
suitors. As for me, the swineherd will lead me
to the town later in the day in the likeness of a
wretched beggar. And if the suitors treat me
evilly in the house, harden yourself to endure
it—even if they should drag me to the door by
my feet, or cast at me and strike me . . . And
another thing I will say to you. If you are indeed my son, let no man hear that Odysseus
has come home. Do not let Laertes know it,
nor the swineherd, nor any of the household,
nor Penelope herself."

12

DOWN TO THE CITY

While father and son sat talking in the hut, the ship in which Telemachus had gone to Pylos reached the town. The suitors learned with dismay that the prince was still alive, and when their own vessel came back they held a meeting. All were angry, but Antinous was angriest of all. He spoke first, being the most eager to devise an evil end for Telemachus.

"Let us slay him in the field far from the city," he proposed, "or somewhere on the roadway. And let us divide his possessions fairly among us but give the house to his mother and whosoever marries her."

But Amphinomus, who of all the suitors was the most pleasing to Penelope because he had an understanding mind, spoke against the plan.

"Friends," he said, "I would not choose to kill Telemachus. It is a fearful thing to slay a son of kings. Nay, first let us seek the counsel of the gods. If the gods are against it, I bid you refrain."

His speech persuaded the rest. So they rose and went to the house of Odysseus and began casting weights and spears on a leveled place in front of the palace. Thus they amused themselves till it was time for them to feast.

The town was a long way from the swineherd's hut. It was evening when Eumaeus came back. The goddess Athene did not intend to let the swineherd recognize Odysseus, for she feared he might tell Penelope. So at his coming she touched Odysseus with her wand and made him into an old man again.

And they supped and slept and rose again and Eumaeus was no wiser.

As soon as it was dawn, Telemachus bound on his sandals and took up his spear. Now, in their counsels it had been agreed that Telemachus must seem to cast Odysseus off and go to the town alone. So the prince said to Eumaeus: "I am bound for the city that my mother may see me, for I know she will never stop grieving till she beholds my very face. But this command I give you, Eumaeus: Lead this stranger to the city that he may beg his food. For I cannot care for every guest who comes to me— I am too troubled in spirit."

Eumaeus looked at his master in amazement. But Odysseus gave the swineherd no chance to speak.

"I, too, my friend, have no great liking to be left behind here," he said. "It is better that a beggar should beg his food in town than in the fields. For I am now too old to stay at the hut and obey the word of the master in all things. Nay, go, and Eumaeus will lead me to the town as soon as I shall be warmed with the fire, and the sun grows hot. For my garments are woefully poor, and I fear that the frost of dawn will overcome me."

So he spoke, and Telemachus passed out of the hut and went quickly home.

With what joy did Penelope come down from her chamber when she heard that her son was in the house! She cast her arms about Telemachus and began to weep, and kissed his face and both his eyes.

"You have come, Telemachus," she said, "a sweet light in the dark. I thought I should never see you again after you had gone in your ship to Pylos, secretly and without my will, to seek news of your dear father. Come, now, tell me, what sight did you get of him?"

But Telemachus would tell her nothing. "My mother," he said, "do not stir the heart within my breast—I have but now escaped from utter death. Go aloft to your upper chamber with your handmaids and vow a sacrifice to all the gods. As for me, I go to the assembly place."

In the hut, meantime, Odysseus waited till the sun was high. Then he bestirred himself to go to the town.

"Be my guide," he said to Eumaeus. "And if you have anywhere a staff ready cut, give it me to lean upon, for truly you said that the way was slippery."

He cast his tattered scrip over his shoulders, and the swineherd gave him a staff. Thus they went on their way, while the dogs stayed behind to guard the hut.

It was late in the day when Odysseus and the swineherd drew near the town and came to the spring from which the people of the city drew water. In this place the goatherd Melanthius met them as he was leading the best of his goats to feast the suitors. He no sooner set eyes on the swineherd and Odysseus than he began to rail at them.

"Now in very truth," he said, "the vile is leading the vile. Where are you taking this glutton, you wretched swineherd—this plaguy beggar, this kill-joy of the feast? If you would give this fellow to me to watch my hut and sweep out the stalls, then he might get food enough to fill his belly. But he will not care to do the labor of the farm. He chooses rather to go louting through the land begging for food.

Now I will tell you. If ever he goes to the house of Odysseus, many a stool will fly about his head and break upon his ribs."

With that he kicked Odysseus on the hip as he went by. Odysseus stood fast upon the path. Black anger filled his heart. He debated whether to rush upon the goatherd and take away his life with the staff, or lift him in his grasp and strike his head against the ground. Yet he hardened his heart to endure.

Eumaeus meantime looked fiercely at the goatherd, and lifting up his hand, prayed aloud: "Nymphs of the well-water, fulfill for me this wish: Oh, that Odysseus may come home! Then, goatherd, right quickly would he scatter all your insolence."

"Lo, now!" Melanthius threw back at him. "What a word has this evil-witted dog been saying! Some day I will take him in a ship far from Ithaca and sell him for a slave. So will he bring me profit. Fool! The day of the returning of Odysseus has gone by!"

With that he stepped along briskly and soon came to the house of the prince. There he went in and sat down among the suitors, opposite Eurymachus, who chiefly showed him kindness.

Meantime Odysseus and the good swineherd drew near the palace. The sound of the lyre rang around them, for the minstrel Phemius was lifting up his voice amid the company in song. Then Odysseus caught the swineherd by the hand and said: "Eumaeus, surely this is the fair house of Odysseus. Right easily might it be known. There is building beyond building, and the court of the house is cunningly made with a wall and battlements."

"Easily you know it," Eumaeus said, "for indeed you never lack understanding. But come, either you go first and join the company while I remain here, or you stay here and I will go in first."

"Go before me, and I will stay here," Odysseus said.

So Eumaeus passed into the house.

13

STRANGER IN
HIS OWN HOUSE

Telemachus was the first to see the swineherd as he came into the hall. Beckoning, the
prince called him to his side. Then Eumaeus
brought over a settle and sat down opposite
Telemachus. And the henchman gave him
meat and bread.

Soon afterward Odysseus entered, leaning
on his staff, and sat down on the broad threshold. Telemachus at once took a whole loaf

out of the basket and as much meat as his hands could hold in their grasp, and said to Eumaeus, "Take and give this to the stranger. And bid him go about and beg of all the suitors in their turn."

Now the minstrel was singing in the hall. So Odysseus took the food and set it on his tattered scrip between his feet and ate sitting on the threshold. But when the song was ended, he rose. Stretching out his hand, he went to each man in turn that he might find out which was righteous and which unjust. The suitors in pity gave him something, wondering at him and asking one another who he was and where he came from.

Melanthius the goatherd spoke up then. "I have seen him before. The swineherd was his guide here."

"O villainous swineherd," Antinous said, "why did you bring this man to the city? Have we not beggars enough who come here and devour the living of your master? Must you call in this man, too?"

The swineherd was about to speak, but Telemachus stopped him. "Truly you take

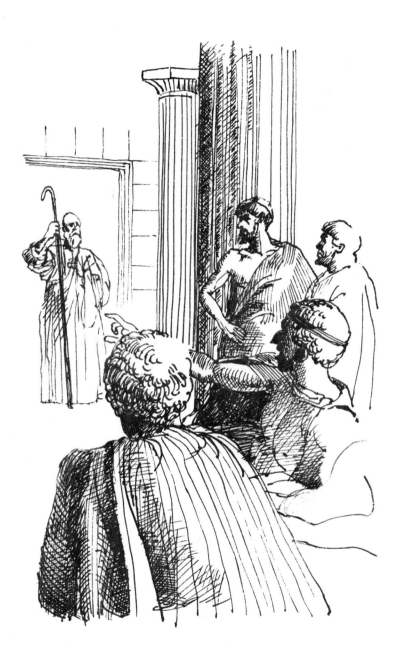

good care of me, Antinous," the prince said, "like a father of his son—you who bid me drive our guest from the hall. God forbid that such a thing should be! Take something and give it to him. Lo, I do not grudge it. I charge you to do it . . . Nay, you will not, for you are far more ready to eat than to give to another."

"Telemachus," Antinous returned, "what word have you spoken? If all the suitors should give him as much as I, he would keep away from this house for three months." So saying he picked up and showed the footstool on which he rested his feet.

Even now Odysseus would have escaped scot-free. But as he was going back to the threshold, he halted by Antinous and said to him: "Friend, give me something. For I think you are not the basest of the Achaeans, but the best man of them all. Therefore you should give me a portion of bread, and a better one than the others."

"What god has brought this plague here to trouble the feast?" Antinous cried. "Stand away from my table, you bold and shameless beggar!"

Odysseus drew back. "Lo now, I see you do not have wisdom with your beauty!" he said. "From your own house you would not give even so much as a grain of salt, you who now sit at another's board and cannot find it in your heart to give me bread where there is plenty at your hand."

Antinous looked fiercely at him. "Now I think you shall not get out with honor from the hall!" he cried. With that he caught up the footstool and struck Odysseus at the base of the right shoulder.

Odysseus stood firm as a rock under the blow. Shaking his head, he went back to the threshold and sat down. "Hear me, you suitors of the renowned queen," he said. "If there be gods and avengers of beggars, may death come upon Antinous before his wedding!"

"Sit and eat your meat in quiet, stranger," Antinous shouted angrily. "Or else go, lest the young men drag you by hand or foot through the house and strip all your flesh off you."

All this time Telemachus said nothing. He sat and nursed his grief. But the news of the deed was quickly carried to Penelope, and she at once sent for the swineherd. "Go, goodly Eumaeus," she said. "Bid the stranger come here that I may speak a word of greeting to him and ask him if he has heard news of Odysseus."

"Queen," Eumaeus answered her, "he would charm your very heart, such things does he say. I kept him three nights and three days in the hut, for he came to me from the ship. He says that he is a friend of Odysseus and has come from Crete, with sorrow by the way. And he insists that he has heard news of him. He says Odysseus is alive in the land of Thesprotia and is bringing many treasures home."

"Go and call him here," Penelope cried, "that he may speak to me face to face! And if I find that he speaks truth, I will clothe him with a goodly mantle and tunic."

So the swineherd went to Odysseus and told him. But he said: "I tremble before the suitors, Eumaeus. Bid Penelope wait till the setting of the sun."

"The stranger is not witless, Eumaeus," Penelope said when he brought back the mes-

sage. "For I think there are no mortal men so outrageous and violent as these."

Telling Telemachus that he would bring boars down in the morning, Eumaeus left the stranger in his care and took the path to his hut.

14

BEGGAR
AGAINST BEGGAR

Then up came a bulky beggar, one Irus, of the town of Ithaca. He was known among all men for his endless eating and drinking. Whenever anyone might bid him, he would run errands. So now he came and would have driven Odysseus from his own house.

"Get you hence, old man, from the doorway," the bulky beggar cried, "lest you be haled out soon by the foot. Do you not see that all are now giving me the wink and bidding me drag you out? Nay, get up, lest our quarrel soon pass to blows."

"Sir," Odysseus replied, looking fiercely at him, "neither in deed nor in word do I harm you. This threshold will hold us both. Do not provoke me too much lest you anger me and, old though I am, I soil your breast and lips with blood."

"Lo now, how trippingly this glutton speaks!" the beggar retorted. "Now I will work my evil will on him and smite him right and left. I will drive all the teeth from his jaws like the tusks of a swine that spoils the corn. Gird yourself."

Now Antinous heard the two and laughed merrily. "Friends," he said to the suitors, "never before has there been such good sport! The stranger and Irus are bidding each other to blows. Quick, let us match one against the other!"

At the words, all leaped up laughing and gathered around the ragged beggars. And Antinous said: "Hear me, you lordly suitors. Here are goats' bellies lying at the fire, that we

laid by at supper time and filled with fat and
blood. Now, whichever of the two wins and
shows himself the better man, let him take his
choice of these puddings."

"So be it!" the others cried and pressed still
closer.

Then Odysseus said: "Friends, an old man,
worn out with trouble, may by no means fight
with a younger. But my belly urges me to
battle. Come now, swear all of you a strong
oath that none, for the sake of showing a favor
to Irus, will strike me a foul blow."

"None will strike you!" Telemachus assured him. "I am your host, and the princes
Antinous and Eurymachus agree with me."

Then Odysseus girt his rags about his loins
and let his great thighs be seen, and his broad
shoulders and breast and mighty arms. The
suitors stared in amazement. "Right soon will
Irus have sorrow of his own bringing," they
said to one another. "Such things that old man
shows from under his rags!"

Irus shook with fear as he looked Odysseus
over and heard these words.

"You lubber," Antinous said to him, "better

for you that you had never been born if indeed you tremble before this man. An old man, too, he is, worn out with trouble. But I will tell you plainly: If this man prevails against you and proves your master, I will throw you into a black ship and send you to the mainland to Echetus, the maimer of all mankind. He will cut off your nose and ears and draw out your vitals and give them raw to dogs to tear."

At this, yet greater trembling took hold of Irus. But they led him into the ring all the same. Odysseus stood there wondering whether he should strike him so that his life should leave his body, or whether he should strike him lightly and stretch him on the earth. And as he thought about it, this seemed to him the better way: to strike lightly, so that the Achaeans might not guess who he was.

The two put up their hands. Then Irus struck at the right shoulder, but Odysseus smote him on his neck under the ear and crushed the bones. Straightway the red blood gushed up through his mouth, and with a moan he fell in the dust and kicked the

ground. But the suitors threw up their hands and roared with laughter.

Odysseus seized Irus by the foot and dragged him out through the doorway into the courtyard. There he set the beggar down and rested him against the courtyard wall and put his staff in his hands, and said: "Sit there now and scare off swine and dogs."

With that, Odysseus put his tattered scrip over his shoulders and went back to the threshold where he sat down.

The suitors went in laughing merrily. "May Zeus, stranger, and all the other deathless gods give you your dearest wish," they said as they crossed the threshold, "seeing that you have made that fellow stop begging in the land!"

Antinous himself set by Odysseus the great pudding stuffed with fat and blood. And Amphinomus took up two loaves from the basket and set them by him. Then he pledged Odysseus in a golden cup, saying: "Father and stranger, hail! May happiness be yours in the time to come!"

"Amphinomus," Odysseus answered him, " you seem to me a prudent man with an understanding mind. Mark, therefore, what I say. I think Odysseus will not much longer be far from his friends and his own land. Nay, he is very near. But for you, may you not meet him in the day when he returns to his own dear country! For not without blood will the suitors and Odysseus part when once he shall have come under his own roof."

He spoke and poured an offering to the gods. Then he drank the honey-sweet wine and set the cup again in the young man's hands. But Amphinomus went back through the hall sad at heart and bowing his head. For his soul boded evil.

15

ODYSSEUS PROVOKES EURYMACHUS

Dark evening came on as the suitors reveled. Presently they set up three braziers in the halls, and on these they laid firewood. Between the braziers they placed torches, which the maids of Odysseus held up in turn to give light.

Odysseus sat watching for a time. Then he rose and said: "You maidens of Odysseus, go to your honored queen and twist the yarn at her side, or card the wools. I myself will hold up the light for all who are here.''

So the maidens went up to Penelope's chamber while Odysseus took his stand by the burning braziers. He held up the torches and gazed on all the men and thought his heavy thoughts.

Then Eurymachus took it in mind to make sport of Odysseus to amuse the lords.

"Hear me, you suitors of the renowned queen!" he said. "I think the torchlight flares from that shining head of his—for there are no hairs on it!" And half in jest and half in earnest he said amid the laughter: "Stranger, would you be my hireling if I would take you for my man at an upland farm? Your wages will be assured you, and there you will gather stones for walls and plant tall trees. I would provide you with bread, and give you clothes, and sandals for your feet . . . However, I think you will not care to go to the labors of the field. You will choose rather to go louting through the land to feed your bottomless belly."

"Eurymachus," Odysseus answered him, "would that there might be a trial of labor between us two—in the spring, when the long

days begin. In the deep grass might it be. And
I should have a scythe and you another like it
that we might try each other in the matter of
labor. . . Or would, again, that there were oxen
to drive, the best there may be, of untiring
strength. And it should be a long field, un-
broken to the plow. Then should you see
whether I would cut a clean furrow or no . . .
Or would that this very day Zeus might waken
war, and that I had a shield and two spears and
a helmet all of bronze, close-fitting on my tem-
ples. Then should you see me mingling in the
forefront of the battle. You would not taunt
me with my belly then . . . Nay, you think
yourself some great and mighty one because
you keep company with a few feeble men. Ah,
if Odysseus might but return! Then right soon
those doors that are so wide would prove all
too narrow for you in your flight!"

Eurymachus was enraged. "Ah, wretch that
you are," he cried, "how boldly you talk! Wine
has got about your wits. Are you beside yourself with joy because you have beaten the
beggar Irus?"

With that he caught up a footstool and

threw it. But Odysseus sat quickly down at the knees of Amphinomus, and the stool struck the cupbearer on the right hand. The ladle dropped to the ground with a clang, while the young man groaned and fell backward in the dust.

Then the suitors began to clamor: "Would that our wandering guest had perished before ever he came here! Now we are all at strife about beggars, and there will be no more joy of the good feast!"

Telemachus sprang up. "Sirs, you are mad!" he cried. "Go home and rest now that you have feasted well. As for me, I drive no man from my hall."

Thus he spoke, and they all bit their lips and marveled at Telemachus in that he spoke boldly.

But Amphinomus said: "Friends, when a righteous word has been spoken, none need be angry. Do not misuse this stranger. Come, let us pour the drink offering and get us home to bed. As for the stranger, let him stay with Telemachus."

So they poured out to the gods, then drank and departed.

16

PENELOPE
AND THE STRANGER

No sooner was Odysseus left alone with Telemachus than he put the torches down.

"Telemachus," he said, looking about him at the shields and spears and helmets that hung upon the walls, "we must lay all the weapons of war in the armory, out of the suitors' way. And when they miss them and ask you about them, say you laid them away so that the smoke should not dim them."

Then Telemachus called his old nurse Euryclea and said to her: "Go, nurse, and shut up the women in their chambers till I shall have laid the goodly weapons of my father in the armory. They have hung in the hall ever since my father went to Troy. The smoke dims them, and I would put them where the vapor of the fire will not reach them."

In pleased surprise the good nurse answered him: "Ah, my child, if you would but take thought like this to guard all the wealth of the house! But who will carry the torch, since you will not have the maidens go before you?"

"This stranger, for I will keep no idle man here."

So Euryclea closed the doors of the chambers. Then they two sprang up and began to carry out the helmets and the shields and the sharp-pointed spears. And Athene cast a most lovely light before them.

"Father," Telemachus said, amazed, "it seems to me that the walls of the hall and the crossbeams and the pillars are bright as if with flaming fire! Truly some god is here!"

"Hold your peace," Odysseus answered

softly. "Keep your thoughts in check and do not ask." And when they had carried out all the weapons and laid them in the armory, he said, "Go and lie down, and I will stay here that I may speak with your mother."

So Odysseus was left behind in the hall. Presently Penelope came. She sat down in her usual chair before the fire while the maidens began to take away the fragments of food, and the little tables, and the cups from which the lords had been drinking. After this they raked out the fire from the braziers onto the earthen floor and piled many fresh logs upon them to give light and warmth. Then at last Penelope said to the housedame: "Eurynome, bring a settle with a fleece on it that the stranger may sit and speak with me."

The housedame hastened to do her bidding. And when Odysseus was seated, the queen said: "Stranger, I will make bold first to ask you this: Who are you of the sons of men? And where is your city?"

"Lady," Odysseus answered her, "no mortal man in the wide world could find fault with you. For lo, the fame of your excellence goes up to the wide heaven. Yet ask me what else you will, but do not inquire about my race and my own country, lest you fill my heart still more with pain. For I am a man of many sorrows. Moreover, it does not become me to sit weeping and wailing in another's house. You may be angry with me and say that I swim in tears as one who is heavy with wine."

"Stranger," Penelope said, "surely my excellence, both of face and form, the gods destroyed in the day my lord Odysseus embarked for Troy. If he might but come and watch over my life, my fame would be fairer and greater. But now I am in sorrow—such a host of ills some god has sent against me. For all the noblest that dwell around Ithaca are wooing me against my will. And I—I waste my heart away in longing for Odysseus. Meantime my parents insist that I marry, and my son chafes that these men devour his livelihood. Thus it is. . . But tell me of your own stock, for you are not sprung of oak or rock, as old tales tell."

Then Odysseus answered her: "Wife of Odysseus, I will tell you what you ask . . . There is a land called Crete in the midst of

the wine-dark sea, and in that land is the mighty city Knossos. Minos began to rule there when he was nine years old. He was the father of my father, Deucalion. Now Deucalion begot me and Idomeneus. And my name is Aethon. I am the younger of the two.

"There in Knossos I saw Odysseus and gave him gifts. For the wind bore him to Crete as he was making for Troy-land. He came up to the city and asked for Idomeneus, saying that he was his friend. But my brother had gone to Troy with the Achaeans. So I led him to the house and gave him good entertainment. Odysseus and his men remained twelve days in Knossos. But on the thirteenth day the wind fell, and then they lifted anchor."

So he told many a false tale, and Penelope's tears flowed fast as she listened. She wept for her dear lord, who even then was sitting by her. And Odysseus, too, longed to weep, but he craftily hid his tears.

"Friend," Penelope said when she had had her fill of weeping and lamenting, "I will make trial of you and learn whether you did in very truth entertain my lord there in your

halls as you say. Tell me what manner of garments he was clothed in, and what manner of
man he was himself, and tell me of his companions that went with him.''

Then Odysseus said to her: "Lady, it is hard
for one so long parted from him to tell you all
this. For it is the twentieth year since he went
there and left my country. Yet even so I will
tell you. Odysseus wore a thick purple mantle,
which had a brooch fashioned in gold. And on
the face of it was a curious device: A hound
held a dappled fawn in his forepaws and gazed
on it as it writhed. All men marveled at the
workmanship, how the golden hound was gaz-
ing on the fawn and strangling it, and the fawn
was writhing and trying to flee. Further, I
noted the shining tunic about his body. It was
like the skin of a dried onion, so smooth it was
and glistening like the sun.

"Moreover, a henchman bore him company,
who was somewhat older than he. I will tell
you of him too, what manner of man he was.
He was round-shouldered, black-skinned, and
curly-headed. His name was Eurybates. And
Odysseus honored him above all his company

because in all things he was like-minded with himself."

So he spoke, and Penelope had yet more desire to weep. For well she knew the sure tokens that Odysseus showed her. Then she said: "Stranger, now you shall be yet more dear and honored in my halls. For it was I who gave him these garments, and folded them myself, and brought them from the chamber, and added, besides, the shining brooch to be his jewel. But him I shall never welcome back to his own dear country."

"Wife of Odysseus, do not waste your heart with weeping for your lord," Odysseus said. "For I tell you: but lately I have heard tell of the return of Odysseus. He is near and yet alive in the fat land of the men of Thesprotia, and is bringing many choice treasures with him. But he has lost his dear companions and his hollow ship on the wine-dark sea. The king of the Thesprotians swore in my own presence that a ship was drawn down to the sea and a company ready to take Odysseus to his own dear country. He is safe, and very near, and will come shortly. I will give you my oath

on it. In this same year Odysseus will come
here, as the old moon wanes and the new is
born."

"Ah, stranger," Penelope sighed, "would
that this word may be fulfilled! I would give
you so many gifts that all who met you would
call you blessed. But my heart has a boding—
Odysseus will not come home any more."

17

THE SCAR
OF THE BOAR

So saying, Penelope turned to her hand-maids. "Wash this man's feet," she said, "and strew a couch for him, bedding and mantles and blankets. And very early in the morning bathe him and anoint him, that he may eat with Telemachus, sitting quietly in the hall."

Odysseus shook his head. "O wife of Odysseus," he said, "truly mantles and blankets are hateful to me since first I left behind me the snowy hills of Crete. And baths for the feet are no longer my delight. Nor shall any of your serving-maidens touch my feet. Unless, indeed, there chance to be some old wife, true of heart, one that has borne as much trouble as myself."

Then Penelope said to him: "I have an ancient woman with an understanding heart, who nursed and tended my lord from his birth. She will wash your feet. Up now, wise Euryclea, and wash this man."

At her words the old woman covered her face with her hands and shed hot tears. "Stranger," she said, "Penelope has bidden me to wash your feet. I will wash them, both for her sake and for your own, for my heart is moved and troubled. Many travel-worn strangers have come here. But I say that I have never seen any so like Odysseus as you are in body, in voice, and in feet."

"That is what all men say who have seen us two," Odysseus answered, "that we favor each other greatly."

The old woman took a caldron and poured in cold water and mingled the warm with it.

Odysseus meantime moved his seat from the
hearth and turned his face to the darkness.
For he had a misgiving that when she handled
his limb, she might recognize the scar of a
wound once dealt him by a boar, and all
should be revealed.

Presently the old woman took the scarred
limb and passed her hands down it. On the
instant she knew the scar by the touch, and in
her excitement she let the foot drop suddenly.
The brass vessel rang as it overturned. The
water spilled on the ground. Joy and anguish
came on the old nurse at the same time,
and her eyes filled with tears, and her voice left
her. She reached up and touched Odysseus on
the chin and whispered: "Yea, truly, you are
Odysseus my dear child, and I did not know
you till I handled the body of my lord!"

She spoke and looked toward Penelope,
meaning to make a sign that her husband was
now home. But Odysseus gripped the old
woman's throat with his right hand and with
the other drew her closer to him.

"Woman, would you destroy me?" he whispered. "Be silent lest another learn the matter

in the halls! For this I declare: You speak at your peril. If the gods let me subdue the suitors, afterward I will not hold my hand from you, though you nursed me at your own breast!"

"My child," Euryclea murmured. "I will keep fast as stubborn stone or iron."

She passed from the hall to bring more water for his feet. And when she had washed him and anointed him well with olive oil, Odysseus again drew his settle nearer to the fire to warm himself and covered up the scar with his rags.

Then Penelope spoke to him again.

"Stranger, there is a thing I will tell you. This thought came to me as though it had been sent me by a god. Odysseus had twelve battle-axes. He would set them up in a row in his halls, standing them far apart, and would shoot his arrow through them all. And now I am minded to offer this contest to the suitors: Whoso shall most easily string the bow of Odysseus in his hands and shoot through all twelve axes, with him will I go and forsake this house—this fair house of my wedlock, which I think I shall evermore remember in my dreams."

Quickly Odysseus spoke up: "Wife of Odysseus, do not delay this contest in your halls. For lo, Odysseus will be here before these men shall have strung his bow and shot the arrow through the iron."

Then Penelope said: "Stranger, if only you were willing still to sit beside me and delight me, sleep would not be shed upon my eyelids. But men may not remain sleepless forever. I will go up to my chamber. And you rest in this house—either strew something on the floor or let them lay bedding for you."

So saying, she rose and went up to her chamber with her handmaids.

18

"I MYSELF
WILL BE THE PRIZE"

At dawn Odysseus went out into the courtyard to make a prayer to Zeus. He saw the
maidens going to the spring for water. He saw
the serving-men split fagots for the fires. Then
into the court came Eumaeus, leading three
fatted boars. The swineherd left them to feed
at large in the courts, and himself went over
to speak with Odysseus.

As they stood talking together, the goatherd

Melanthius drew near, leading his best goats to be a dinner for the suitors. He tied the beasts under the gallery. Then he said to Odysseus: "Stranger, will you still plague us here in the hall with your begging? I think we two will not be parted till we taste each other's fists."

Odysseus answered him never a word. In silence he shook his head.

Then a third man came up, the cowherd Philoetius. Ferrymen had brought him over from the mainland with a heifer and fatted goats for the suitors. He carefully tied the cattle under the gallery and drew close to Eumaeus and began questioning him: "Swineherd, who is this stranger? Unfortunate as he is, he looks like a royal lord."

With this he offered his right hand in welcome, saying: "Father and stranger, hail! May happiness be yours in time to come, though now you are held fast in many sorrows! The sweat broke out on me when I beheld you, and my eyes stand full of tears for memory of Odysseus. Alas! He, too, I think, is clad in such vile garments and is wandering among men—if yet he lives. I was but a lad when he set me over his cattle. But it is grievous now to watch over the herds. Long ago I would have fled and gone to some other of the proud kings, for things are now past bearing. But still my thought is that Odysseus might come home and make a scattering of the suitors in the halls."

"Cowherd," Odysseus answered him, "I see that you have an understanding heart. Therefore I will tell you something and swear a great oath to confirm it. Be Zeus my witness that while you are still in this place, Odysseus will come home, and you will see with your eyes the slaying of the suitors who lord it here."

"Ah, stranger, would that Zeus might fulfill this word!" the cowherd answered. "Then you should know what my strength is, and how my hands follow to obey."

When the suitors had gathered in the hall, the three went in. Telemachus was inside, waiting for his father. He bade Odysseus sit down on a settle by the threshold and placed a little table for him. And by him he set a mess of entrails and poured wine into a golden cup.

Presently Penelope came down from her upper chamber. She stood by the pillar of the

roof, holding up her glistening attire before
her face, and a faithful maiden stood on either
side of her. The eye of every suitor was upon
her as she spoke:

"Hear me, you lordly suitors, who have
vexed this house that you might eat and drink
here evermore! Seeing that all your desire is to
wed me, I will put you to a contest and I myself will be the prize. I will set forth for you the
great bow and battle-axes of divine Odysseus.
And whoso will most easily string the bow in
his hands and shoot through all twelve axes,
with him will I go."

So saying, she commanded Eumaeus to set down the bow and the axes of gray iron which with her own hands she had taken from the storeroom.

"This will be a terrible contest!" Antinous said. "For I think that this bow does not lightly let itself be strung. Nor is there a man among us as Odysseus was. I myself saw him. I remember it well, though I was still but a child."

He said this, but in his heart he hoped that he would string the bow and shoot through the axes.

Proudly Telemachus looked at his beautiful mother. "See the prize which is set before you!" he said. "A lady the like of whom there is not now in the Achaean lands! Come, make no excuse. And I myself would like to make trial of this bow. If I string it and shoot through the axes, then I shall not sorrow if my lady mother quits these halls, for I shall be left behind well able now to lift my father's goodly combat gear."

With that he cast off his scarlet cloak and sprang to his full height and took the sword from his shoulders. First he dug a good trench

and set up the axes, one long trench for them
all. He made the line straight and stamped in
the earth around the ax heads, and the iron
rings on the ax handles stood upright. Amazement fell on all to see how neatly he set the
axes though he had never seen it done.

He went and stood by the threshold and began to try the bow. Three times he made it tremble in his great desire to bend it, and three times he rested from his efforts. And now at last he might have strung it, but Odysseus nodded, frowning, and stopped him. Then the prince said: "Lo, now even to the end of my days I shall be a weakling. Or it may be that I am yet too young. But come, you who are mightier men than I. Try the bow and let us make an end of the contest."

He set the bow on the ground, leaning it against the doors and propping the shaft against the bow-tip. Then he sat down once more.

Antinous said, "Rise up in order, my friends, beginning from the left."

Then first Leiodes stood up, who was their soothsayer. He alone hated their violent deeds and was indignant with all the suitors. He took the bow and the shaft and stood by the threshold and tried the bow with his unworn, delicate hands. But he could not bend it.

"Friends," he said, "of a truth I cannot string it. Let someone else try."

With that he leaned the bow against the doors and propped the shaft against the bow-tip.

"Of a truth," Antinous said, "there are others who will draw it soon. Melanthius, light a fire in the halls. Place a great settle by the fire and put a fleece upon it, and bring a great ball of lard that we young men may warm and anoint the bow with the lard."

So Melanthius kindled the fire and drew up a settle and put a fleece on it and brought a great ball of lard. The young men warmed the bow and tried it. But they could not string it, for they did not have the strength. Yet Antinous and Eurymachus still kept trying.

Meantime, at a sign from Odysseus, the cowherd and the swineherd went out of the house and Odysseus passed out after them. Outside the gates and the courtyard, they drew close. Then, looking earnestly at his companions, Odysseus said: "Cowherd and swineherd, what manner of men would you be to help Odysseus if he should come suddenly? Would you stand on the side of the wooers or of Odysseus? Tell me."

For answer, the cowherd lifted up his eyes and prayed: "Father Zeus, if you would fulfill this wish: Oh, that he might come! Then should you know what my strength is, and how my hands follow to obey!"

Eumaeus, too, prayed to all the gods that Odysseus might return to his own home. And when Odysseus knew they would stand by him, he said: "Behold, I have come home, even I. After many trials I have come in the twentieth year to my own country. And I know that my coming is desired by you alone of all my thralls, for from none besides have I heard a prayer that I might return once more to my home. And now I will tell you all the truth. If the god will subdue the proud suitors to my hands, I will bring you each one a wife and will give you land of your own and a house built near to me. You two shall therefore be in my eyes as brothers and companions of Telemachus. But look now that you may know me well and be sure in heart—behold the wound that the boar dealt me with his white tusk long ago!"

With that he drew aside the rags from the

great scar. When the two saw it, they threw their arms around Odysseus and began to weep and kissed him lovingly on head and shoulders. And Odysseus kissed their heads and hands. Then he said: "Let us go in now, one by one, I first and you following. The suitors will not let me try the bow. Do you, then, Eumaeus, as you bear the bow through the hall, set it in my hands. And speak to the women that they bar the doors of their chamber and stay in silence at their work no matter what din they hear. But on you, Philoetius, I lay this charge: to bolt and bar the outer gate of the court."

So saying, he passed into the house and sat down on his settle. The two thralls went in behind him.

19

ODYSSEUS BENDS THE BOW

Now, Eurymachus was handling the bow, warming it on this side and on that at the fire. Yet even so he could not string it. And he said: "Lo, I grieve that we are so far worse than Odysseus in strength."

"Eurymachus," Antinous answered him, "you forget that today is the feast of the archer god Apollo. Who at such a time would be bending bows? Nay, set it quietly by. In the morning bid Melanthius the goatherd to lead here the very best goats in all his herds that we may sacrifice to Apollo the archer. Then we will try the bow and quickly make an end of the contest."

The words pleased the suitors. So they fell to drinking. And when they had drunk to their hearts' content, Odysseus spoke out among them.

"Hear me, you suitors of the renowned queen," he said, "and mainly I make my prayer to Eurymachus and godlike Antinous. Give me the bow that I may prove my hands and strength."

All grew angry at this, for all were afraid he would string the bow.

"Wretched stranger, you have no wit, no wit at all," Antinous said. "Are you not content to feast at ease in our high company and listen to our talk? I declare, if you string the bow, you will find no kindness at the hands of anyone in our land. We will send you to Echetus, the maimer of all men, and you will not be saved alive from him. Drink at your ease and do not strive with men who are younger than you."

But here Penelope spoke up. "Antinous," she said, "do you think that if the stranger strings the great bow of Odysseus he will lead me to his home and make me his wife? Nay, he himself, I think, has no such hope in his breast."

"Wise Penelope," Antinous answered her, "far be such a thought from us. What we dread is the speech of men and women. People will say: 'Truly, men far too mean are wooing the wife of one that is noble. They could not string the polished bow. But a stranger and a beggar came in his wanderings and lightly strung the bow and shot through the iron.' "

Then Telemachus said: "My mother, as for the bow, mine alone is the right to give or deny it to whomso I will. If I should choose to give this bow to the stranger once and for all, to bear away with him, none should stop me. But go to your own chamber and bid your handmaids ply their tasks. The bow shall be for me —for all, but for me in chief, for mine is the lordship in the house."

So in amazement she went back to her chamber.

Now, the swineherd had taken the bow and was carrying it to Odysseus when the suitors all cried out upon him. Eumaeus stood still in fright. But Telemachus from the other side of the hall spoke threateningly to him, saying, "Eumaeus, bring the bow here! You shall soon be sorry that you serve many masters!"

Then the swineherd bore the bow to Odysseus and set it in his hands. And he called the nurse Euryclea and bade her bar the doors of the women's chamber. At the same time Philoetius hastened from the house. He barred

the outer gates of the fenced court and made
fast the gates. Then he returned to his seat.

Odysseus was handling the bow, turning it
every way about and testing it on this side and
on that, to see if worms might have eaten the
horns. And suddenly, all without effort, he
bent the mighty bow and took it in his right
hand and tested the bowstring, which rang

sweetly at the touch. Then great grief came
upon the suitors, and the color of their faces
changed.

Odysseus caught up an arrow which lay by
his table, bare. He took and laid it on the
bridge of the bow, and held the notch, and
drew the string, right from the settle on which
he sat. With straight aim he shot the shaft. He

did not miss one of the axes, beginning from the first ax handle. The shaft passed clean through all the rings and out at last.

Then Odysseus said: "Telemachus, your guest does you no shame. I did not miss my mark. But now it is time that supper, too, be got ready for the Achaeans, while it is yet light."

He nodded with bent brows. And Telemachus girt his sword about him, and took the spear in his grasp, and stood by his high seat at his father's side.

20

FOUR AGAINST ALL

Odysseus stripped off his rags and leaped to the great threshold with his bow and his quiver full of arrows and poured out all the shafts before his feet.

"Lo, this terrible trial is ended at last," he cried. "Now I will know another mark, which man has never yet struck."

With that he pointed the bitter arrow at Antinous.

Now, that prince was about to raise to his lips a golden cup, and death was far from his thoughts. For who among men at a feast would think that one man amongst so many would bring foul death on him? But Odysseus smote him with the arrow in the throat, and he fell sidelong, and the cup dropped from his hand.

With a wild clamor the suitors leaped from their seats. They peered everywhere along the walls—but nowhere was there a shield or spear to lay hold of. Then they shouted angry words at Odysseus: "Stranger, utter doom is assured you now! For you have slain the man that was far the best of all the noble youths in Ithaca, and vultures shall devour you here!"

But Odysseus looked fiercely on them and said: "You dogs! You said in your hearts that I should nevermore come home. You wasted my wealth and traitorously wooed my wife while I was yet alive. You had no fear of the gods. But now the bands of death have been made fast upon you one and all."

Pale fear took hold of all, and each man looked about him where he might escape. Eurymachus alone answered him.

"If you are indeed Odysseus of Ithaca come home again, you speak with right of all that the Achaeans have done in your halls," he said. "However, he now lies dead who is to blame for all—Antinous. For he brought all these things upon us. It was not that he longed very greatly for the marriage but that he desired to be king over all the land of Ithaca. And now he is slain as he deserves. But spare your people. And we will make amends for all that has been eaten and drunk in your halls."

Odysseus looked fiercely at him. "Eurymachus," he said, "not even if you gave me all that you now have and whatever else you might add to it, not even so would I hold my hands from slaying. Now the choice lies before you—whether to fight in fair battle or to fly."

He spoke, and their knees grew weak. Then Eurymachus turned to the suitors.

"Friends," he cried, "it is plain that this man will not hold his hand, but will shoot from the threshold till he has slain us all. Therefore let us take thought of battle. Draw your blades and hold up the tables to ward off the arrows. And let us all have at him with one accord and drive him from the doorway. Then we will go through the city. Quickly will the cry be raised—and this man will have shot his last shaft."

He drew his two-edged sword and leaped on Odysseus with a terrible cry. But in the same moment Odysseus shot the arrow and struck him on the breast and drove the shaft into his liver. Eurymachus let the sword drop from his hand. Bowing over the table, he fell across it, and the food and cup spilled on the ground.

Then Amphinomus drew his sword and made at Odysseus to drive him from the door. But Telemachus was beforehand with him, and smote him from behind with a spear between the shoulders, and drove it through the breast. He fell with a crash and struck the ground full with his forehead. Then Telemachus sprang away, ran quickly to his father and said: "Father, I will bring you a shield and two spears and a helmet. When I return, I will arm myself and give arms to the swineherd and the cowherd."

"Run and bring them while I have arrows to defend me," Odysseus said.

Telemachus ran, took from the armory four shields and eight spears and four helmets, and came quickly to his father. He put the gear about his body, and the two thralls armed themselves and stood beside Odysseus.

So long as he had arrows to defend him, Odysseus kept aiming, and the suitors fell thick one upon another. But when the arrows were gone, he leaned his bow against the doorpost, and slung his shield about his shoulders, and bound on his head a helmet with horse-hair crest. And in his hands he grasped two mighty spears.

Now, there was in the wall a certain little door raised high above the floor. Here was a way into an open passage. Odysseus bethought himself of this and bade the swineherd stand near that door and watch the way, for there was but one approach to it.

Then the prince Agelaus said, "Friends, will not some man climb to the postern door and let the people know?"

"It is no use, Prince Agelaus," Melanthius said. "The gate of the courtyard is terribly high—you cannot let the people know. Moreover, the entrance to the passage is perilous. One valiant man might keep back a host. But come, let me bring you armor from the inner chamber, for I think that is where Odysseus and his son put the arms."

With that Melanthius climbed up by the transept of the hall to the inner chambers of Odysseus. He took twelve shields and as many spears and helmets and brought them speedily and gave them to the suitors.

Odysseus' heart grew faint within him when he saw them putting on the armor and brandishing the long spears in their hands. Quickly he said to Telemachus: "I am sure that one of the women is stirring up an evil battle against us. Or perchance it is Melanthius."

"Father," Telemachus answered him, "it is I that am to blame, for I left the door of the chamber open, and one of them has been quick to spy it. Go now, Eumaeus, and close the door of the chamber and see if it is Melanthius."

"Tell me," the swineherd said, "shall I slay him if I prove the better man?"

Odysseus answered him: "Telemachus and I will hold the suitors here, for all their fury. But you and the cowherd tie his feet and arms behind his back and cast him into the chamber, and close the doors after you. Make a rope fast to his body and drag him up the lofty pillar till he is near the roof beams."

The goatherd did not hear them coming as he searched the room for armor in the secret place of the armory. They stood waiting for him on either side the doorposts. With a hel-

met in one hand and a shield in the other, he
came toward them. And as he crossed the
threshold, they rushed on him and caught him,
and dragged him in by the hair. They bound
him hand and foot, tightly winding each limb
behind his back. Then they fastened a rope to
his body and dragged him up the lofty pillar
till he came near the roof beams.

So he was left there, bound. But they two
got into their armor and closed the door, and
went to Odysseus. There they stood, breath-
ing fury, four men by the threshold, while
those others were many and good warriors.

21

ATHENE KEEPS HER PROMISE

Then Athene drew near them in the likeness of Mentor, Odysseus' friend. And Odysseus was glad when he saw her and said: "Mentor, ward off hurt from us, and remember me, your dear companion who befriended you often!"

So he spoke, knowing well that it was Athene. But the suitors were deceived.

"Mentor," they all shouted, "do not let Odysseus beguile you to fight against us! It will be the worse for you if you do!"

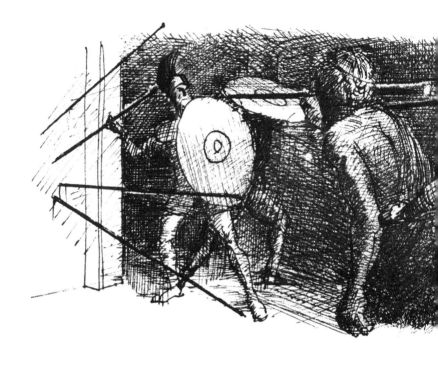

At this Athene was mightily angered, and she said to Odysseus, "Come here, friend, and stand by me."

But for a while she would not give him the victory in full—first she made trial of the might and valor of Odysseus and his son. Then she flew up to the roof timber of the hall, as a swallow flies, and there sat down.

Seeing "Mentor" gone from the threshold, Agelaus spoke among the suitors that were left: "Friends, now at last this man will hold

his unconquerable hands. Lo, now Mentor has left him, and these remain at the entrance of the doors alone. Therefore do not throw your spears all together. Do you six cast first and smite Odysseus. And as soon as he shall have fallen, we will take care of the rest."

So they cast their spears eagerly. But Athene caused one to smite the doorpost of the hall, and another the door, and made the spear of yet another suitor stick fast in the wall. So when they had avoided all the spears, Odysseus said, "Friends, now my word is that we, too, cast and hurl into the press of the suitors that are mad to slay us."

So they all took good aim and threw their spears. Each one hit its mark. Four men dropped to the floor, and the suitors fell back into the inmost part of the hall. But the others dashed upon them and drew out the shafts from the bodies of the dead.

Once more the suitors threw their spears eagerly. But Athene caused them to be thrown in vain. Then again Odysseus and his men cast into the press, and once more four suitors fell.

At this moment from the roof Athene held high her destroying shield. Terrified, the suitors fled through the hall like a drove of cows that the gadfly falls upon and scatters in the springtime. But the others set on them like vultures, smiting right and left through the hall. And there arose a hideous moaning, and the floor ran with blood.

Struggling through to Odysseus, Leiodes clasped him by the knees. "I entreat you by your knees, Odysseus! Show mercy on me and have pity!" he cried. "I am the soothsayer among the suitors! I have done no evil!"

Odysseus looked askance at him and said: "If indeed you are the soothsayer among these men, you must often have prayed that I might not return and that my dear wife should follow you and bear you children. Therefore you shall not escape the bitterness of death." With that he caught up a sword and drove it clean through his neck.

Now, Phemius the minstrel, who sang among the suitors by force, still sought how he might avoid black fate. He stood by the postern with his lyre in his hand. But suddenly he laid the lyre on the ground and sprang forward and clasped Odysseus' knees. "I entreat you by your knees, Odysseus! Show mercy on me and have pity!" he prayed. "It will be a sorrow to yourself in the aftertime if you slay me who am a minstrel and sing before gods and men. Telemachus will testify that not by my own will or desire did I sing to the suitors at their feasts. But being so many and stronger than I, they forced me."

Telemachus heard him. "Father, hold your

hand," he cried, "and do not wound this blameless man! And let us save also the henchman Medon, who always had charge of me in our house when I was a child."

As Telemachus spoke, Medon rose up quickly from under the seat where he was hiding with an oxhide around him. He caught the young prince by the knees. "Friend," he pleaded, "here I am! Stay your hand, I pray you! And speak to your father, lest he harm me with his sword!"

Odysseus smiled. "Take courage," he said, "for he has saved you. Go and sit down in the court, you and the minstrel, till I have accomplished all that I must needs do in the house."

With that he went peering all through the house to see if any man was yet alive and hiding away to avoid his fate. But he found all fallen in the dust and heaped one on another, like fishes that the fishermen have drawn forth in the meshes of the net from out the gray sea.

22

HUSBAND AND WIFE

All this time Penelope had slept, for Athene had caused a deep sleep to fall upon her. But when Melanthius had been dispatched and the women had helped carry out the dead, the nurse Euryclea went up to call her mistress.

"Awake, Penelope, dear child," she said when she stood above her lady's head, "that you may see with your own eyes that which you desire day by day! Odysseus has come home! He has slain the proud suitors!"

"Dear nurse," Penelope answered her, "the gods have marred your reason. Why do you mock me and speak wild words and rouse me out of slumber?"

"I mock you not, dear child!" Euryclea said. "Odysseus is here! He is that stranger whom all the suitors railed at. Telemachus knew long ago that he was in the house, but he hid it that his father might take vengeance on the haughty suitors."

Then Penelope leaped from her bed and fell on the old woman's neck and let the hot tears fall. "Come, dear nurse, tell me truly," she said. "If indeed he has come home as you say, how has he slain the shameless suitors, he being but one man and they so many?"

"I did not see," the nurse replied. "I only heard the groans of the dying. Then your son called me out, and I found Odysseus standing among the dead, who lay stretched on the floor around him one upon another. And now all are gathered in a heap by the gates of the court while he is purifying his house with brimstone. He has kindled a great fire, and has sent me to call you. So come with me that you may both enter into your hearts' delight."

But Penelope shook her head and her heart beat fast. "This is no true tale," she said skeptically. "It is one of the deathless gods that has slain the proud suitors. Odysseus is lost far away."

"My child, your heart is ever slow to believe," the old nurse said. "With my own eyes I saw the scar that the boar on a time dealt him with his white tusk. I spied it while washing his feet and would have told you, but he laid his hand on my mouth and would not let me say a word. Come with me! I will stake my life on it!"

Then Penelope went down. But her mind was in a maze. She did not know whether she should stand apart and question her dear lord or draw near and clasp and kiss his head and hands. Undecided, she crossed the threshold and sat down opposite Odysseus in the light of the fire by the further wall.

Now, he was sitting by the tall pillar, looking down and waiting to know if his noble wife would speak to him. But she sat long in silence. First she would look steadfastly at him, and then again she did not recognize him because he was clad in rags.

"Mother," Telemachus said at last, "why do you turn away from my father? No other woman in the world would harden her heart thus."

"Child," she answered, "my mind is amazed within me. I have no strength to speak nor to ask him anything, nor to look on him face to face. But if in truth this is Odysseus, verily we shall know each other surely, for we have tokens that we two know, secret from all others."

Odysseus smiled. Quickly he said to Telemachus: "Let your mother make trial of me. I am filthy and clad in vile rags, and therefore she will not yet allow that I am he . . . But, son, let us take counsel," he went on, "how all may be for the very best. You know that we have slain the men who were most notable of all the noble youths in Ithaca. I beg you to consider the feud that will be taken up."

"Father," Telemachus answered him, "they say that your counsel is far the best among men. What do you think?"

"I will tell you," Odysseus answered. "Let the minstrel with his lyre in hand lead off the measure of the mirthful dance. Whoever of the town hears the sound will think that here we have a wedding feast. Thus the slaughter of the suitors will not be known before we have time to get to our farmland. After that we shall consider what to do."

So presently the great hall rang with the sound of dancing feet. And all who heard the music and the noise thought, "Surely some one of the many wooers has wedded the queen."

Meanwhile the housedame Eurynome had bathed Odysseus and anointed him with olive oil and cast a mantle and a tunic about him. As he sat before Penelope, he glowed with beauty and grace. But she gazed at him and said no word.

"Strange lady," Odysseus said at last, "no other woman in the world would harden her heart to stand thus aloof from her husband, who after many trials has come to her in the twentieth year."

"Strange man," she answered, "I have no proud thoughts. But I know right well what manner of man you were when you went out of Ithaca on the long-oared galley. Come, Euryclea, spread for him the good bridal bedstead, the bedstead that stands outside the bridal chamber."

She said this to make trial of her lord. But, frowning with anger, Odysseus said: "This is a bitter word, lady, that you have spoken. Who has set my bed elsewhere? Of all men there is none living, however strong, that could lightly move it. I know, for I built it myself. There was an olive tree growing in the inner court, and its trunk was as large as a pillar. Round about this tree I built the chamber. I roofed it over well and added doors, well fitted. Then I cut off all the branches and rough-hewed the trunk, and smoothed it, and fashioned it into the bedpost.

"I do not know, lady, if the bedstead is yet in its place, or if some man has cut away the trunk of the olive tree and set the bedstead elsewhere."

He spoke, and Penelope's heart melted within her as she knew the sure tokens that Odysseus showed her. Then she ran straight

to him and, weeping, cast her arms about his neck and kissed his head.

"Do not be angry with me, Odysseus," she said, "because I did not welcome you straightway. For always my heart shuddered for fear lest some man should come and deceive me with his words. But now that you have told me all the sure tokens of our bed, you bend my soul."

Odysseus wept as he embraced his beloved wife and true. And even as the sight of land is welcome to swimmers whose ship has been wrecked upon the deep, so welcome to Penelope was the sight of her lord. And she could never quite let go her arms from his neck.

Then at last Odysseus said: "Lady, we have not yet come to the end of all our labors. Still there will be toil, long and difficult, that I must bring to a full end. Therefore come, lady, let us to bed, that we may at once take our joy of rest beneath the spell of sweet sleep."

23

LAERTES

When dawn came, Odysseus quickly rose, for there were heavy things upon his mind.

"Lady," he said, "the news about the wooers whom I slew will quickly get abroad. Therefore go into the upper chamber with the women and sit there and look at no man nor ask any question. And I will go to the upland farm to see my father."

He put on his armor and roused Telemachus and the cowherd and the swineherd, bidding them take weapons. So they armed and, spears in hand, followed him.

Climbing all the way, the four men quietly approached the farm. But only the Sicilian woman who cared for Laertes was in the house. "Go in," Odysseus bade his companions. "Quickly sacrifice the best of the swine for the midday meal. Meantime I will make trial of my father, whether he will know me again when he sees me." And giving them his weapons of war, he climbed up to the terraced vineyard.

Laertes was alone, digging about a plant. He was clothed in a filthy tunic, worn and patched, with leggings of oxhide about his legs and long sleeves lapping over his hands.

When Odysseus saw his father so wasted with age and so careless of his dress, he stood still and let fall a tear. But then, controlling himself, he went forward. Laertes did not look up. He kept on digging about the plant.

"Old man," Odysseus said, "whose thrall are you, and whose garden do you tend? Tell me also if this is indeed Ithaca that I have come to. I met a man on the way who said this was Ithaca, but when I asked him about my friend, whether he is alive or dead, he would not tell me. Once I treated kindly a man who came to our home. He told me he was from Ithaca and said that his father was Laertes. I led him to our halls and gave him good entertainment. Such gifts, too, I gave him as are the due of guests."

Laertes looked up at last, and his eyes streamed fast with tears. "Stranger," he said in a broken voice, "you have indeed come to that country which you ask about. But violent men hold it. And he is not in Ithaca—that ill-fated guest of yours and my son. Far from his country's soil the fishes, it may be, have devoured him in the deep sea, or he has fallen prey to birds and beasts upon the shore. But come, plainly tell me all: How many years have passed since you entertained him? Moreover, tell me truly: Who are you of the sons of men? Where is your city?"

"I will tell you all most plainly," Odysseus answered. "From out of Alybas I come, and I am the son of Apheidas, the prince, and my

own name is Eperitus. But as for Odysseus, this is now the fifth year since he departed out of my country.''

Grief seized the old man. Groaning, he clutched the dust and ashes with both his hands and showered them on his gray head.

At the sight, the sharp sting of sorrow throbbed up through Odysseus' nostrils. He sprang toward his father and fell on his neck and kissed him, saying: ''Behold, I, my father, am the man of whom you ask. In the twentieth

year I have come to my country. I will tell you
all clearly, though there is great need of haste.
I have slain the suitors in our halls and
avenged their bitter scorn and evil deeds."

Laertes did not return the kisses. He stood
before Odysseus all confused. "If you are indeed my own child," he murmured, "show me
now some token that I may be assured."

"Look first on this scar," Odysseus said,
"that on a time the boar dealt me with his
white tusk. But come, I will even tell you the
trees which you gave me once for my own
when I was begging you for this and that, being but a child and following you through this
very garden. Pear trees thirteen you gave me,
and ten apple trees, and figs two score. And as
we went, you named the fifty rows of vines you
would give me."

So he spoke, and the old man's heart melted
within him, for he knew the sure tokens that
Odysseus showed him. He threw his arms
about his dear son, and Odysseus caught him,
fainting, to his breast.

But Laertes came to himself quickly. "My
son," he said, "my heart is afraid lest all

the men of Ithaca come up against us here."

"Take courage," Odysseus answered, and led the way down to the house.

There they found Telemachus and the cowherd and the swineherd carving meat and mixing wine. The Sicilian handmaid bathed Laertes. And when she had thrown a clean mantle about him, they sat down to eat.

Now, the old woman had gone and called the thrall Dolius and his sons from their labor. Coming in and seeing Odysseus, they stood still in great amazement, for they guessed at once who he must be. Then with a glad cry Dolius ran toward him, both hands outstretched. "Beloved," he said, grasping the hand of Odysseus and kissing it on the wrist, "hail to you and welcome, and may the gods give you all good fortune!" The sons of Dolius also gathered about Odysseus and greeted him well and clasped his hands.

"Forget your marveling," Odysseus said, "for there is need of haste." And he bade them all sit down to meat.

So they were busy with the meal in the house.

24

"LET PEACE AND ABUNDANCE BE THEIR PORTION"

Rumor had meantime swiftly gone about the city, telling the tale of death. The people heard it and gathered from every side before the house of Odysseus. Sighing and groaning, each brought out his dead and buried them. But those that came from other cities they placed on ships and sent with fisherfolk, each to his own home. As for themselves, the people went together to the assembly place.

When all were gathered there, Eupeithes rose and spoke among them. For deep grief lay on his heart for his son Antinous.

"Friends, a great deed truly has this man devised against the Achaeans! Some he led away on his ships, and lost his ships and lost his company. Others again — and those far the noblest — he has slain on coming home. Up now! Let us go forth! We shall lose face for ever if we do not avenge ourselves on the slayers of our sons and of our brothers. Let us be going, lest these fellows be beforehand with us and get over the sea!"

Pity fell on the Achaeans as they saw him weeping. Then Medon came near them, and the minstrel Phemius, whose lives Odysseus had spared. The two stood in the midst of the gathering, and Medon spoke, saying:

"Hear me now, you men of Ithaca! Surely Odysseus did not plan these deeds without the will of the gods. Nay, I myself saw an immortal god who stood by Odysseus in the shape of Mentor. I saw him cheer Odysseus on. Then the deathless god stormed through the hall, and the suitors fell thick one on another."

At his words fear came on the people. Old Halitherses rose. He remembered well how Telemachus had asked their aid and they had denied it.

"Hear me now, you men of Ithaca," the old man said. "These deeds have come to pass through your own cowardice. For you allowed your sons to continue their foolish ways. They did a great villainy, wasting the wealth of Odysseus and holding his wife in no regard. But now obey my counsel. Let us not go forth against him, lest some among us may find a death of their own bringing."

So he spoke. But the greater part of the people leaped up with a cry. For his counsel was not to their mind. Swiftly they rushed for their armor. And when they had put it on, they assembled in front of the town. Eupeithes led them.

Now the goddess Athene saw all this, and her concern was for Odysseus and for old Laertes, whom of all men on earth she loved the most. So she sped to high Olympus and said to Zeus: "O Father, tell me: What thought is now in your mind? Will you yet further rouse up evil war and the terrible din of battle? Or are you minded to make these people friends again?"

"My child," Zeus answered her, "all this is of your own making. But I will tell you what is best. Now that Odysseus has taken vengeance on the suitors, let the people make a firm agreement with him. Let Odysseus be king all his days. And let us bring about forgetting the slaying of their children and brothers. So may both sides love one another as of old, and let peace and abundance be their portion."

At these words, Athene came glancing down from the peaks of Olympus. Meantime at the house of Laertes they had finished the meal.

"Let one of you go out and see," Odysseus said, "if the peple are already drawing near against us."

A son of Dolius at once ran to the threshold. And lo, they were close at hand! Then he cried out: "Here they are, close upon us!"

They sprang up and put on their armor, Odysseus and his three and the six sons of Dolius. Laertes and Dolius also armed themselves, gray-headed though they were. The thralls flung open the gates and all went out, Odysseus leading them.

Then Athene drew near them in the likeness of Mentor, and Odysseus knew her straightway. She came and stood beside Laertes. "Oh you who are dearest of all my friends," she said, "swing your long spear aloft and hurl it!"

With that the goddess breathed great strength into him. Then Laertes swung his long spear aloft and hurled it. It struck Eupeithes full on his helmet. The spear went

clean through, and he fell with a crash, and his arms rattled about his body. Then Odysseus and his son fell on the foremost fighters with their swords and two-headed spears. And now they would have slain them all had not Athene called aloud and stopped all the host of the enemy, crying out: "Hold your hands from fierce fighting, you men of Ithaca, that you may be parted quickly without bloodshed!"

Pale fear seized them. At the voice of the goddess, the arms flew from their hands and fell on the ground. They turned their steps to the city as men eager for life, while Odysseus threw himself upon them like an eagle.

But at that moment Zeus cast a flaming bolt. It fell at the feet of the gray-eyed goddess.

"Son of Laertes," she said to Odysseus, "hold your hand now lest Zeus be angry with you!"

Odysseus obeyed. And he was glad. Far more to his liking were the scythe and the plow than sword and spear . . .

Thereafter Athene made peace between them. They sacrificed to the immortal gods. And far-wandering Odysseus ruled in Ithaca all the days of his life.

GLOSSARY

ACHAEANS   (A-kee'-uns), a branch of prehistoric Greeks

ACHILLES   (A-kil'-eez), a hero who fought against Troy

AETHON   (Ee'-thon), a false name of Odysseus

AGELAUS   (A-jel-ay'-us), a suitor

ALCINOUS   (Al-sin'-o-us), King of the Phaeacians

AMPHINOMUS   (Am-fin'-o-muss), a suitor

ANTINOUS   (An-tin'-o-us), a suitor

APHEIDAS   (A-figh'-duss), a prince whose son Odysseus pretends to be

APOLLO   (A-pol'-o), god of light and healing

ARETE   (A-ree'-tee), wife of King Alcinous

ATHENE   (A-thee'-nee), goddess of wisdom and helper of heroes

CALYPSO   (Ka-lip'-so), a nymph

CICONES   (Sik'-o-neez), a people whose city Odysseus sacked

CIRCE   (Sir'-see), a beautiful witch who turned Odysseus' men to swine

CLYTONEUS   (Kligh-to'-nyoss), son of King Alcinous

CYCLOPES	(Sigh-clo′-peez), a race of one-eyed giants
CYCLOPS	(Sigh′-clops), one-eyed giant
DEMODOCUS	(Dem-od′-o-cuss), a blind minstrel
DEUCALION	(Du-kay′-lee-on), son of King Minos of Crete
DOLIUS	(Do′-lee-us), a thrall of Laertes
ECHETUS	(E-kee′-tuss), a cruel king who maimed people
EPERITUS	(E-per-igh′-tuss), a false name of Odysseus
EUMAEUS	(You-mee′-us), a swineherd loyal to Odysseus
EUPEITHES	(You-pigh′-theez), father of the suitor Antinous
EURYALUS	(You-ree′-a-luss), an athlete who insults Odysseus
EURYBATES	(You-ri-bay′-teez), a comrade of Odysseus
EURYCLEA	(You-ri-klee′-ah), Odysseus' old nurse
EURYMACHUS	(You-rim′-a-cuss), a suitor
EURYNOME	(You-rin′-o-mee), Penelope's housekeeper
HALITHERSES	(Hal-i-thur′-seez), an old nobleman of Ithaca
HALIUS	(Hal′-i-us), son of King Alcinous
HELEN	(Hel′-en), wife of King Menelaus of Sparta

IDOMENEUS	(I-dom'-i-nyoos), king of Crete who fought against Troy
IRUS	(Eye'-russ), a beggar
KNOSSOS	(Noss'-os), a city in Crete
LAERTES	(Lay-ur'-teez), father of Odysseus
LAOCOÖN	(Lay-ok'-o-on), a Trojan priest
LAODAMUS	(Lay-o-day'-muss), son of King Alcinous
LEIODES	(Ligh-o'-deez), a suitor who was soothsayer to the rest
MEDON	(Mee'-don), a servant in Odysseus' house
MELANTHIUS	(Mel-an'-thee-us), a disloyal goatherd
MENELAUS	(Men-e-lay'-us), king of Sparta
MENTOR	(Men'-tor), a leader in Ithaca
MINOS	(Migh'-nos), an ancient king of Crete
NAUSICAA	(Naw-sik'-ay-ah), daughter of King Alcinous
NESTOR	(Nes'-tor), king of Pylos
NOMAN	(No'-man), a false name of Odysseus
ODYSSEUS	(O-dis'-yoos), king of Ithaca
PENELOPE	(Pe-nel'-o-pee), wife of Odysseus
PHAEACIANS	(Fee-ay'-shuns), an island people who befriended Odysseus
PHEMIUS	(Fee'-mee-us), minstrel to the suitors

PHILOETIUS	(Fil-ee'-shus), a cowherd loyal to Odysseus
PHOENICIANS	(Fe-nee'-shuns), a sea-going people of Asia Minor
POSEIDON	(Po-sigh'-don), god of the sea
PRIAM	(Pry'-am), king of Troy
PYLOS	(Py'-los), a city in southern Greece
SINON	(Sigh'-non), a cousin of Odysseus
SIRENS	(Sigh'-rens), creatures part woman, part bird, who lured mariners with song
TELEMACHUS	(Te-lem'-a-cuss), son of Odysseus
THESPROTIANS	(Thes-pro'-shuns), people of a land northwest of Greece
TROJANS	(Tro'-juns), people of Troy
ZEUS	(Zoos), king of heaven

ABOUT THE AUTHOR

Anne Terry White was born in the Ukraine, but her family came to the United States when she was eight years old. She grew up in New England, graduated from Brown University, and later took a master's degree at Stanford University in California.

When the author was still a child, an older sister told her about the archaeologist Heinrich Schliemann and his exciting discovery of the ruins of Troy. Later Homer's *Odyssey* and *Iliad* were among her favorite books. The idea of writing a book for young readers about Odysseus has long been in her mind.

Mrs. White is the author of more than thirty books for boys and girls, ranging in subject matter from archaeology and astronomy to Shakespeare. She has also adapted many classics and translated a number of modern books from the Russian.

Anne Terry White lives in Stamford, Connecticut. She has two daughters and several grandchildren.

ABOUT THE ILLUSTRATOR

Arthur Shilstone's painting and drawing assignments have led him to South America, Hawaii, Wake Island, and Tokyo, as well as to many parts of this country. He is well known for his magazine illustrations, book jackets, and commissions for industrial companies.

A native of New Jersey, Mr. Shilstone was graduated from Pratt Institute in Brooklyn, New York. He studied at the Brooklyn Museum Art School and at the New School for Social Research, where he later taught evening classes. His work has apppeared in many exhibitions, and he has received two awards at the Society of Illustrators Annual Show.

Mr. Shilstone lives in West Redding, Connecticut, with his family.